CULTURE AND
MENTAL DISORDERS

CULTURE AND
MENTAL DISORDERS

By

RALPH LINTON

Sterling Professor of Anthropology
Yale University
New Haven, Connecticut

Edited by GEORGE DEVEREUX

Director of Research, Devereux Foundation
Devon, Pennsylvania

CHARLES C THOMAS • PUBLISHER
Springfield • Illinois • U.S.A.

CHARLES C THOMAS • PUBLISHER
BANNERSTONE HOUSE
301–327 East Lawrence Avenue, Springfield, Illinois, U.S.A.

Published simultaneously in the British Commonwealth of Nations by
BLACKWELL SCIENTIFIC PUBLICATIONS, LTD., OXFORD, ENGLAND

Published simultaneously in Canada by
THE RYERSON PRESS, TORONTO

Library of Congress Catalog Card Number: 56-6395

Printed in the United States of America

Preface

In selecting a scientist to present the relationship of psychiatry to cultural anthropology, the Salmon Committee turned to Professor Ralph Linton whose contributions to this field have been outstanding. His lucid style of writing and his facility of verbal expression made his influence far-reaching. It was my privilege to join in a conference with Dr. Linton and Dr. Edwin Zabriskie, the Chairman of the Salmon Committee, in which Linton's ideas relating to psychopathology and psychiatry were discussed at length. It was a privilege to listen to his critical and stimulating presentation and we looked forward to the lectures and to his book with great expectancy. It was unfortunate that Dr. Linton's health interfered with the completion of his work. It was fortunate that his former student and loyal friend, Dr. George Devereux, was able to edit the lectures in a form which does justice to Dr. Linton. Having attended these lectures, I was gratified to read this book which so ably presents Dr. Linton's thinking.

OSKAR DIETHELM, M. D.
Professor of Psychiatry
Cornell University Medical College

v

Contents

CULTURE AND
MENTAL DISORDERS

I

Culture and Normality

THE NATURE OF CULTURE

Culture has often been defined as "the sum total of human achievement." This is a philosophical definition which is of no use for the purposes of this book. Moreover, it is hardly necessary to say that the concept of culture used here does not refer to the ordinary usage, designating "the finer things of life" such as reading Browning and playing the piano. Throughout this book I will use the concept of culture in its technical, anthropological sense.

Since the old and long-established definition of culture as "the sum total of human achievement" is operationally useless for the anthropologist, he speaks of cultures, in the plural. When the anthropologist uses culture in the singular, he refers to processes which are to be found in many cultures and can therefore be regarded as characteristic of Culture as a distinct phenomenon.

Each society has its own culture, which can be defined briefly as its "way of life." The tendency which some social scientists and historians fall into of using the terms "society" and "culture" interchangeably is regrettable, and results in considerable confusion. Actually, society is simply an organized group of individuals. Culture, on the other hand, is an organized group of ideas, habits and

Much of the research for this book was done under a grant given by the Wenner-Gren Foundation for Anthropological Research to the Institute of Human Relations at Yale University to be administered by Dr. Linton. Grateful acknowledgment is made for this generous aid in the study of personality and culture.

conditioned emotional responses shared by the members of a society. In practice, society and culture are always linked, since, without culture, a group of individuals is not a society but merely an aggregate. A big football game may bring together thousands of people united by a common interest and reacting in unison to stimuli, such as long end runs or a touchdown, but when the game is over, the aggregate dissolves. Societies must be together long enough to develop techniques of living and working together. The organization of *all* societies and the existence of *any* society as such depends upon culture. It is the sharing of ideas, habits, attitudes, etc. which makes it possible for a group of individuals to organize and to function as a society. To keep this distinction quite clear, we might say that the agencies involved are different. Societies are people, while cultures exist on a psychological and behavioral level. Both societies and cultures are continua. They persist through time and have normally a much longer life span than any individual. Both are largely self-perpetuating. This persistence of both society and culture is, from the point of view of society, based upon the *training* of the individuals; when viewed from the point of vantage of the individual, it is based upon *learning*. Hence learning mechanisms are of tremendous importance in any attempt to correlate personality and culture. This point should be borne in mind in anticipation of our subsequent discussion of certain basic problems in the formation of the ethnic or basic personality.

The structuring of society is actually an aspect of culture, since society, as a continuing organization, is made up of positions, or statuses, which are occupied by a series of successive individuals or groups of individuals, whose relations to other positions, or other statuses, can only be defined in terms of the reciprocal rights and duties that exist between the holders of statuses.

We may say, then, that cultures have both content and organization, both of which are present at every point in time and also throughout the entire time dimension. The content of cultures consists of the ideas and behavior of society's members, though this is not what we think of when we are dealing with Culture as a concept. We must therefore stop for a moment and consider the manner in which this concept comes into being, or is constructed.

Since there are no identities anywhere in the universe, no two situations, no two behaviors, etc. are identical. In fact, the general semanticists will even point out that no one is the same individual at any two instants of his life. Yet, even though there is no real identity anywhere, neither is there infinite variety. What we do observe is a wide range of similarities. Thus, although no two situations which serve as stimuli to individual behavior are ever identical, many situations are very much alike, and it is in terms of these similarities that human beings operate by equating different situations with the forms of behavior that, customarily, go with them.* Briefly stated, while the behavior of the members of a society will vary with respect to a particular type of situation, these variations will be within a definite and finite range. This *range* is what we call the *real* culture pattern, as distinct from Culture as a construct.

The generalized picture which the ethnographer gets from a series of behaviors, or responses to a particular

---

* The classical example is, of course, the legal process, which operates extensively in terms of precedent, though no two legal situations arising in life are truly identical. [*Ed.*]

situation, is what I call the *culture construct pattern.* I
hasten to add that I am using the term "pattern" in accordance with its long-established usage, which is more
limited than is the way in which it was used by Dr. Ruth
Benedict in her *Patterns of Culture* (3). The sum total
of these construct patterns, which we record as "the culture," is what we anthropologists mean when we are
talking about the culture of a particular society. These
construct patterns represent the *modes of variation* in the
behavior of the members of that group in response to
what *they* consider similar situations.*

The point to be retained is that the *real pattern* of
behavior is, in every case, not a single point; it is a *range*
within which observed behaviors fall. This range is a
particular finite range, and, by falling within this range,
behavior becomes effective socially and realistically, with
respect to a particular type of situation.

It is this generalized picture which I call the *culture
construct pattern*, and what is included in it is the *mode
of the range of variations at the point of maximum frequency*. As we shall see, these construct patterns are of
great importance for personality studies.†

---

* A very homely example of this is the initial way in which some of the
Plains Indian tribes dealt with the newly imported horse. The Crow
called it "the magic dog" [the dog being their only real domestic animal]
and promptly hitched the horse to the travois, a means of transporting
goods which consisted of two poles, the ends of which dragged on the
ground, while the tops were crossed over the back of the beast of burden.
This device was designed for the dog as a transport animal. Likewise,
when the horse was first imported into the Near East, where the long
established beast of burden was the ox, the horse was primarily used as
a draft animal and therefore, as we learn from Homer, was driven not
with a whip but with a goad. [*Ed.*]

† The logical problems involved in the *construction* of these patterns
from observed behavior has been discussed in some detail by Devereux
(*14, 15*).

Except for a few brief references to the problems of status and position, I spoke in the preceding pages as though all members of a society were mutually interchangeable, i.e., as if all of them defined situations by and large in the same manner and responded to them more or less similarly. This, needless to say, is not the case. The individual participates in the culture of his society to the extent required by his social roles. Every culture includes a series of ideas, values, and patterns of behavior with which all members of the culture must be familiar. Language is one of these.*

In addition to such patterns, familiar to all members of a society or culture, there are many other skills which are known only to a limited number of individuals, even though these skills contribute materially to the well-being of the entire society. The skill of the physician is an example of such special knowledge, possessed by one group of persons within a culture.

The content of the culture of any homogeneous society can be divided into three categories, on the basis of the extent to which the elements within each category are shared by the society's members.

First, there are those ideas, habits and conditioned emotional responses which are common to all sane, adult members of the society. We will call these *Universals*. It

---

* It may be argued, of course, that in some societies there is a special "women's language" or "children's language," or else "directional speech," the vocabulary and structure of which is determined by whether one addresses a superior, an equal or an inferior. These facts are correct, of course, but do not invalidate the thesis that language is shared by all members of a society. Indeed, even though a culture may contain special vocabularies for the use of women, this language must be understandable to the men. The most obvious example is the fact that even though, ordinarily, the American *male* has no occasion to *use* the expression "my husband," he understands it perfectly well. [*Ed.*]

must be understood that this terminology applies only to the content of a particular culture. An element classed as a Universal in one culture may be completely lacking in another. To this category belong such elements as the use of a particular language, the tribal patterns of costume and housing, and the ideal patterns for social relationships. This category also includes the associations and values which lie, for the most part, below the level of consciousness but which are, at the same time, an integral part of the culture.

Second, we have those elements of culture which are shared by the members of certain socially recognized categories of individuals but which are not shared by the total population. We will call these *Specialties.* Under this head come the patterns for all those varied but mutually interdependent activities which have been assigned to various sections of the society in the course of its division of labor. In all societies certain things are done by, or known to, only a designated part of the population, although they contribute to the well-being of the whole. Thus all women within the tribe will be familiar with certain occupations and techniques, while the men will be familiar with a different series. As a rule, the men will have only a rather vague general knowledge of the things which belong in the women's province and vice versa. Under this head there can also be classed the activities which the society has assigned to special craftsmen or functionaries, such as the smith, carpenter, doctor and priest. . . The uninstructed do not know the full details of procedure, but everyone has a general knowledge of how [these things are done] and will be resentful of inferior workmanship and suspicious of innovations. Any departure from the accustomed procedure or failure to achieve the expected results brings an emotional reaction.

Third, there are in every culture a considerable number

of traits which are shared by certain individuals but which are not common to all the members of the society or even to all the members of any one of the socially recognized categories. We will call these *Alternatives*. The elements of culture which may be included in this class have a wide range, varying from the special and often quite atypical ideas and habits of a particular family to such things as different schools of painting or sculpture. Aside from the nature of participation in them, all these Alternatives have this in common: they represent different reactions to the same situations or different techniques of achieving the same ends. The cultures of small societies living under primitive conditions usually include only a moderate number of such *Alternatives* while in a culture such as our own they are plentiful. Examples of such *Alternatives* for ourselves would be such things as the use of horses, bicycles, railroad, automobiles and airplanes for the single purpose of transportation; our variety of teaching techniques, or our wide range of beliefs and attitudes toward the supernatural.

Beyond the limits of culture there lies still a fourth category of habits, ideas and conditioned emotional responses; that of *Individual Peculiarities*. These include such things as one person's abnormal fear of fire, due perhaps to some accident of his early experience. . . . . Every individual has certain peculiarities of this sort, whether he is a member of a primitive tribe or a modern urban community, and the sum total of such individual differences within any society is enormous. Individual Peculiarities cannot be classed as a part of culture, in the sense in which the term is ordinarily used, since they are not shared by the society's members (*41*, pp. 272–4).

It is obvious from the foregoing that the relation between the individual and the culture of his society is a reciprocal one. He is both shaped by it and, in turn, contributes to its shaping. We shall, first of all, consider in some detail the cultural influences exerted upon the developing individual—in other words, how the behavior of *other* individuals, acting in a culturally prescribed way, influences the development of the growing child.

Broadly speaking, the influences can be grouped under three headings:

(1) *What other people do to the individual.* This category includes, first and foremost, techniques of child care and child training.

(2) *What other people consciously teach the individual.* This category includes the whole range of what is commonly referred to as "instruction."

(3) *The* BEHAVIOR *of other people, as* OBSERVED *by the individual.* This category is frequently ignored in studies of child development, especially in those which focus their attention too exclusively upon actual, observed technical procedures in child care. Devereux (*15*), in particular, has systematically stressed the ability of the child to compare the treatment *he* receives with that received by *others,* and he has emphasized that not the least important aspect of this comparison is the emotional tone characteristic of the adult who performs a culturally standardized child training manipulation.* It seems self-evident that the child's comparison between his experiences and those of other children is an important factor in the development of its self-evaluation and in determining the emotional affect characteristic of concrete parent-child relationships.

---

* In a recent paper, written in response to criticisms of her views on swaddling, Margaret Mead (*50*) likewise reaches the conclusion that the impact of child care is greatly influenced by the attitude of those who perform these technical operations. [*Ed.*]

Cultural influences on the formation of the normal ethnic or basic personality are particularly important in the early years of life, though the exact period during which the maximum influence is exerted is still undetermined. Recent research seems to indicate that the predominant role assigned to early infantile experiences by certain schools of psychoanalysis is not supported by evidence: nursing, toilet training, etc., seem to be much less significant as determinants of personality than was formerly supposed. Such at least appear to be the conclusions to be drawn from the findings of Sewell (56), and Orlansky (52). However, it should be stressed that these studies were focussed primarily on actual *technical operations,* without a correspondingly detailed study of the maternal attitudes which accompanied these performances. Unobserved or ignored differences in attitudes accompanying the motor acts of nursing, weaning or toilet training may, as Devereux suggests, be far more crucially important than are actual nursing schedules, the date at which the baby is weaned, or the suddenness with which it is toilet trained. In addition, the conformity or nonconformity of the infantile experiences of a given child with the usual experiences of other children in a given society probably also has a deep-going influence on the manner in which actual nursing, weaning and toilet training experiences affect the child's development. Thus, I recall Devereux telling me that a Plains Indian analytic patient of his, who, by Western standards, was weaned late—i.e., at the age of one year—felt a savage resentment over having been denied the breast too soon, since by the standards of the culture children are nursed longer than this (16).

Directly related to this problem is the matter of the critical period in development during which cultural factors exert the greatest influence on personality formation. Many anthopologists have agreed with certain schools of psychoanalysis that the crucial time in personality formation is early childhood. However, I am inclined to agree with Devereux's recent views (15) that cultural influences may have their greatest effect during the oedipal period, at least with regard to the formation of the *socially most relevant segment* of personality. He states his views on this point as follows:

> The effort to understand the basic personality *primarily* in terms of *baby* and *infant* care techniques is a futile one. In stressing almost exclusively the experiences of the pre-oedipal stage of psychosexual development, one tends to disregard the very crucial experiences of the oedipal periods, and, *a fortiori,* of the pubertal period, during which the oedipal conflict is once more faced and, in many cases, more or less successfully resolved. Indeed, the oedipal and pubertal stages of life are of special significance for the adjustment of the individual to society, since the manner in which the oedipus complex comes into being and is resolved determines to a large extent not merely man's manipulation of his culture, but, above all, the nature of his relation to other human beings, *as real persons and not merely as sources of purely narcissistic pre-oedipal gratification.* In addition, it is self evident that, as the child matures, the segments of the culture pattern mediated to it through cultural experience expand rather rapidly. Thus the child becomes increasingly capable of seeing—or, at least, of effectively sensing—the cultural forest behind the trees of discrete, atomistic experiences with individual culture traits. In other words, only the broadening of the child's cultural experience enables it to detect the pattern,

ethos, value system, means-end schema, etc., which give a meaning and a structure to his discrete experiences. When seen in this context, the thesis that baby, infant, and child-care techniques exert an *appreciable* influence on the personality only if they are closely connected with, and easily derivable from, the tribal ethos, ceases to be merely an axiom and becomes susceptible of verification. Indeed, the adaptation and adjustment of the baby, infant or child to the expectations and training techniques of its environment, and its response both to its training and to those who train it, can, during the pre-oedipal period, only be narcissistic and sadomasochistic. Hence, they can lead neither to genuine relations to real human beings, nor to a meaningful and constructive manipulation of the segments of culture which these persons mediate to the infant. Only after the child is old enough for these early impressions, expectations, rules, etc. to acquire a meaning and reveal a pattern, can they be *accepted*—though with certain pregenitally determined distortions—instead of being merely *endured,* and only then can the human beings who reared it become *persons,* instead of remaining "partial objects" which are merely sources of narcissistic gratifications, or of blows to the infant's self-esteem.

It is therefore felt that the decisive force in personality formation is the ethos, which gives meaning to discrete culture traits, rather than the individual culture traits, e.g., training techniques, themselves. The determining force of the latter depends primarily on the extent to which they reflect the over-all ethos and pattern of the total culture. This means that the basic personality is formed *primarily* during the oedipal and pubertal periods, *whose resolving eliminates or sublimates earlier pregenital traits and urges* (*15,* pp. 45–6).

Another point of importance is whether the original start given the budding personality in childhood is, or is not, supported by subsequent experiences. Some types of influence unquestionably continue throughout life. In a stable culture this influence is rather toward the reinforcement of already established personality patterns than toward the evolving of new patterns. By contrast, in a rapidly changing culture, the change in influences and the difference between the personality-shaping influences experienced in childhood as contrasted with those experienced in adulthood, as a result of cultural change, can be an appreciably disorganizing factor, as all acculturation studies tend to show (43).

It is implicit in what we just said that cultural influences upon the individual are paralleled by the influence which the individual exerts on culture. This latter type of influence manifests itself chiefly through the acceptance or rejection of new cultural items. Indeed, it is chiefly in adulthood that the individual is free and able to accept or reject new ideas, new appliances, etc., thus determining whether or not these new cultural items will be integrated into his society's culture.*

CULTURE AND PERSONALITY

Since all members of society are exposed to much the same cultural influences, subject mainly to status differences, one might expect to find certain uniformities in the personalities of members of a particular society. At the same time, one would not expect to find a general identity. Leaving out possible factors of physiological difference for the moment, the individuals exercising the culturally pat-

---

* Needless to say, this applies quite as much to new items borrowed from other cultures through acculturation as to new items resulting from the internal development or progress of the individual's own culture. [*Ed.*]

terned behaviors toward the developing child will differ in their precise interpretation of the culture pattern, with correspondingly different effects on the individual children. Given cultural differences, one would also expect to find differing personality norms for various societies. Observations employing projective tests and other objective techniques have shown this to be the case. Of course, all types of personality configurations will differ enormously from one society to another. The personality configuration of maximum frequency in a particular society at a particular time is termed its ethnic or basic personality. Other terms, such as modal personality, national character, etc., embody approximately the same idea. Except in societies whose cultures are undergoing a rapid change, the basic personality will be congruous with the culture and will permit individuals sharing it to participate in the culture with a minimum of frustrations and a maximum of rewards (*44*).

We will show in the third part of this introductory lecture that these facts have an important bearing upon the appraisal of precisely what constitutes normality. However, in order to lead up to that important question, we must first seek to clarify more in detail the entire problem of the influence of culture upon personality, which we barely touched upon in the first part of this lecture.

The concept of a "personality type" related to a society is an ancient one. The oldest theories on this matter were essentially biological and explained the differences between the basic personalities characteristic of two societies in terms of biological heredity. This view was disproved by Boas (*4*) and the whole school of anti-racist anthropologists. However, these critics failed to account for observed differences in national character—and such an

explanation may not altogether disregard *a priori* all hereditary factors. For example, heredity may be quite important in the personality formation of a small endogamous
group. Thus, we find that there are differences in the
degree of activity displayed by infants in the Southwestern United States. The White infant in the Southwest is
more active than is the child born into the adjoining, but
culturally very different Hopi tribe (10). In these cases
we may suspect hereditary factors to be responsible for
observed differences, even though the anti-racists are un-
willing to concern themselves with hereditary factors
which may possibly be of importance for personality.

Edward Sapir (55) and Ruth Benedict (3) started the
study of basic personality or national character by means
of a psychological approach. (I will not concern myself
here with certain early European psychoanalytic attempts
at explaining culture, because such attempts often did not
recognize the importance—and sometimes not even the
existence—of social differences.) Even though in our discussion we will emphasize chiefly psychological factors
related to culture, we will always be mindful of the possible hereditary influences upon personality formation,
which may be reflected in the inheritance of certain skills
or potentialities. Thus, it would seem that certain endogamous groups sometimes produce a few persons with
special skills, such as phenomenal memories, with fairly
reliable regularity.

One approach to the study of personality as shaped by
culture was the attempt to characterize cultures themselves psychologically. Sapir (55) used the polar concepts of introvert and extrovert to characterize cultures,
most of his data on which he based these characterizations

having been obtained through insight. However, instead of continuing in this direction, Sapir finally came to the conclusion that each individual had his own distinct culture, which resulted in a failure on his part to see culture as a patterned whole—as a set of mutually adjusted behaviors and attitudes.

Benedict (3), in turn, used the concept of patterns of culture and a somewhat different dichotomy: the conceptual pair, Apollonian and Dionysian, rather than Sapir's extrovert-introvert dichotomy. According to Benedict's scheme, the Apollonian is characterized by an intellectual approach to life and by low emotional affect. The Dionysian, in turn, is characterized by a high emotional affect and by ecstatic experiences. The Zuni and other Pueblo Indians lent themselves almost perfectly to an illustration of the Apollonian concept, since formal ritual permeated large sections of individual life in those tribes. However, she was unable to find a tribe which fitted the Dionysian pattern as well as the Zuni fitted the Apollonian one.

In seeking to appraise Benedict's contribution to culture and personality problems, we must remember that she was characterizing cultures and not individuals. In addition, her work did not involve accurate studies of individuals, by means of life histories and the like. Hers was a characterization of *cultures*—and large questions can be raised, and, indeed, have been raised, as to the accuracy of certain of her characterizations. Furthermore, although it is always a culture as a whole which she characterizes, there is always the implicit, though never stated, assumption that the *average individual* within that society would have a personality with characteristics of the general sort which the *culture* would seem to represent. This, however, does not necessarily follow.

Let us take one example: the Kwakiutl. I assume that nowadays most students of human behavior have read Benedict's *Patterns of Culture,* which is a delightfully written book that holds conviction until you begin to analyze it in detail. In this work the Kwakiutl are characterized as a megalomaniacal society. It is quite certain that the behavior of the chiefs of this tribe is such that if it occurred in a European country, in a modern European society, it would be characterized as megalomaniacal.

What we must bear in mind in sizing up the Kwakiutl situation is the fact that, in order to acquire the property which the chiefs used in competitive and self-aggrandizing potlatching—and potlatching was almost entirely the chief's business—it was necessary that the surplus created by all the non-chiefly members of the chief's sub-tribe be funnelled into the chief's hands, so that he could use it for these ostentatious distributions of wealth. We might also remark that these distributions of wealth were not quite as "crazy" as they sound at first, since any "gift" which the Kwakiutl chief made in this manner, he received back within a year with a 100% interest. In a way, the potlatch of the Kwakiutl was really more like a forced loan, and the property which was used for this purpose, and for a very ostentatious, but actually not very large scale, destruction of property, served to show how wealthy one really was, etc. Now, it is quite evident that the so-called megalomaniacal behavior of the chiefs required that there be also other individuals, making up about 85% of the population of the tribe, who not only were not megalomaniacal, but were actually a lot more cooperative than is the average individual in our society.

To be sure, these non-chiefly producers, who funnelled

wealth into the chief's hand, derived a vicarious satisfaction from the display of their chief, through an identification with him. The chief's violent expression of his hostilities, and his rise in the social scale which was achieved through potlatching, were, in a sense, acts performed by him as a representative of his sub-tribe, which also enhanced the social position of his sub-tribe within the tribe as a whole. However, even if we concede this, it nonetheless seems out of the question to characterize the *bulk* of the Kwakiutl tribe as megalomaniacal.

The same strictures many also be applied to Benedict's other characterizations of *cultures* as implicit means of characterizing the modal *personality* of the members of the respective tribes. This observation holds true particularly of her characterization of the people of Dobu. It seems highly questionable whether the actual Dobuan individual was a paranoid personality. We might well ask at this point: precisely what constitutes paranoia? After all, if I were to walk through a lonely street in Harlem at 2:00 A.M. and saw three men coming toward me meaningfully and purposefully, I would not regard it as paranoid on my part if I got away from there as fast as I could. And, in a place like Dobu, where the people are very good poisoners, even if they don't call it poisoning but magic (*21*), when you are living with a group who dislike you heartily and who would benefit by killing you, you are not so much paranoid as realistic if you are worried over the situation and over your safety. In brief, we might say that such characterizations of *cultures*, which represent *faits accomplis* cannot, without much additional research, be used as a basis for the psychological characterization of the *individual members* of the societies in question.

Having disposed of the difficulties of deriving an operationally adequate view of the actual basic personalities of the individuals composing a society from a psychological characterization of their cultures, we can now turn our attention to dynamic studies of various primitive individuals belonging to a variety of tribes.

The first set of dynamic studies was the work on child training among non-Europeans done by Margaret Mead (47). It was directed particularly toward accounting for the existence of certain attitudes in adults, or rather, it represented an attempt to study the formation of the total personality. Mead got an excellent start on this work, until three things happened. One of these was that she was strongly influenced by the success of Benedict's *Patterns of Culture* so that when she went to Bali to work she was seeking *a single dominant attitude* by which the culture could be characterized (2).

The second factor was that, by the time that Mead returned from Bali, there had been further developments made in this field. This new frame of reference for the study of the relationship between culture and personality was quite different from the one which had inspired her field work and in support of which her field data had been collected. Hence, when she put this material to a use which differed from the one for which it had been intended, she often simply did not have all the data needed for the documentation of her more recent views.

The third factor of some importance was Mead's increasingly feminist slant (49). I would say that Mead, using the psychological approach, was attempting to do for women what Boas had attempted to do for socially submerged racial groups. That is, she was trying to rescue them from their low estate by pointing out, and even by proving definitely, that there were no significant differences between the sexes, or at least only such differences as would inspire envy in the male. Indeed, an English friend of mine, who had just finished reading *And Keep Your Powder Dry* (48), remarked to me that he didn't realize why this picture of American society seemed so strange to him until he realized that none of the children in the book seemed to have any fathers.

One can see this feministic point of view emerging in such books as *Sex and Temperament* (47). For example, in her description of the Tchambouli we are presented with perfect pictures of hard-working, hard-headed females with esthetically oriented husbands who spend their time dancing and making masks. Unfortunately, her demonstration would have been more convincing if she had also explained the fact that the Tchambouli had been driven out of their territory by neighboring tribes and were returned to it under British protection, with the definite understanding that any tribe which attacked them would incur the wrath of the British administration. As a result the Tchambouli men, who had previously spent their time in warfare for the protection of their group, found themselves with nothing to do, although the women's work continued in the same pattern. Although I have not done any work with the Tchambouli, I suspect that the situation was similar to that of the Plains Indians after they were put on the reservation. As late as 1875, the Plains Indians man devoted 80% of his time and 90% of his interest to the arts and practice of war. When these were taken away, there was nothing left for him to do but dance. Many of the young men, who were living at the end of the last century, committed suicide from sheer boredom.

Shortly after these earlier attempts, Abram Kardiner became interested in this type of research and attempted something in the line of dynamic studies. He worked, as a matter of fact, with both Ruth Benedict and Ruth Bunzel for one year, but came up against many difficulties, since the approach of Benedict and Bunzel was not a dynamic one and consisted chiefly in the characterization of societies as a whole. They had not collected data on specific techniques of child training, or on the specific requirements that the culture made on the individual at various points in the life cycle. The next year Kardiner and I joined forces and gradually, over some seven years in which we cooperated, we developed a certain set of techniques of approach for the study of these problems (*30, 32*). I certainly would not claim that they represented the last word. However, they seemed to be the best that we could do under the circumstances and with the material which was then available. You must remember that at the time that this work began there were only about a half dozen cases in which projective tests had been given to members of non-European groups. The life-history material up to that time was also highly limited; the sort of thing that had been published were biographies such as Radin's *Crashing Thunder* (*54*)—the story of a Winnebago who, when he went on the warpath, went by way of the Illinois Central Railroad—or nearly so. There was also a very interesting biography of a Fox woman by Michelson (*51*), which is rather short, and a series of biographies of Plains Indians. These last were characterized by statements of one paragraph on the subjects' childhood, culminating in such a remark as, "at the age of fourteen I went on my first war party," and

from then on mostly mentioning matters of war. Sometimes, the narrator would inject a sentence on personal life,
such as, "After my sixth war party I got married for the
first time," and then would describe another war party.
There was nothing to work on when it came to getting a
picture of how the individual in a primitive society really
thought and felt. Hence, what Kardiner and I were trying
to do was to find out something about the dynamics of
personality formation. We tried in particular to discover
whether information from societies, whose culture patterns
differed so widely from our own, would offer confirmation,
or otherwise, of ideas that the psychoanalysts developed
regarding the influence on personality formation of particular patterns of child training, these theories being
based on clinical material obtained from members of our
own society.

In addition, we also wanted to see whether there were
really such things as "basic personality" types. I chose
the term basic personality in preference to "tribal
character" or any one of a half dozen terms which have
been used with the same general meaning, because I at
least recognized from the start that the behavior, and
even the attitudes, expected from different individuals in
different statuses and different positions within the society,
differed considerably in many respects. My idea was that
if there was a common denominator of personality it had
to be something which underlay these various status configurations, of attitudes; something which would be congruous with all such diverse configurations and yet would,
in a way, be basic to the whole lot of them. It would represent and constitute that sort of personality organization
and content which underlay these various status personali-

ties. In addition, it seemed necessary to find out whether
this basic personality was present in any significant
majority of the members of a given society. Now, as I
said at the start, at first we simply didn't have the data
which would have enabled us to get at the fundamental
and highly personal material. What we did have, however, were fairly good cultural accounts, the first of which
I provided as a basis for discussions. I have been taken
to task since, on the grounds that when I was in the field
I was not collecting material with an eye to this problem.
I wasn't. However, in each case the societies which I
described were societies which I felt I knew fairly
intimately, where I had actually lived with groups, in two
or three cases for two years each, was an adopted member
of a native family and had known a lot of people, not as
ethnological subjects, but as friends or enemies, on the
basis of well developed inter-personal modifications of the
culture patterns. In other words, I felt that I knew what
I was talking about. As the work went on, several of our
graduate students at Columbia University were sent out
specifically to get the type of information we wanted.
The most important work of this sort was done by Dr.
Cora Dubois, who, by that time, was no longer a student.
She did for our group her *The People of Alor* (19) which,
I would say, is still the best cultural-psychological study
made of any "primitive" group.

In the first stages of this study, the cultures were treated
without relation to individuals, or to a status breakdown.
We took the culture as a whole, and deduced from this
material the sort of personality which would find life in
a society with this kind of culture congenial and easy. We
tried to define the type of personality which apparently

could adjust to this cultural situation with a minimum amount of difficulty.

This task is not as complicated as it may sound. I am getting ahead of myself a little here and will refer only briefly to the matter of status personality. We usually find that in any society the culture is actually dominated by the activities of some particular group. This is the type of activity which anthropologists usually record about a tribe, since it is the thing that seems most important in that society and culture. Yet, to take the Plains Indians once more as an example, it was, after all, only a small percentage of the tribe which went on the warpath; only men between, shall we say, the ages of fourteen and sixty. Although, this is quite a slice of the population, it would not represent more than one third of the total. Nonetheless, the whole interest of the tribe was focused on this warlike activity and everything was organized to facilitate the activity of the warriors and to give them peace of mind and entertainment when they came home. Wives were supposed to devote their entire time to husbands home from the warpath, leaving the old folks to take care of the children and the housekeeping. It would be impossible, however, to arrive in this way at a characterization of the culture in a *single psychological term*, although one could say that Plains culture embodied such and such values, in such and such order of importance. Hence one could proceed to say also that an individual who had the personality characteristics which fit this value scale would have to be either aggressive or docile to feel at home in this culture. It was tough for men, because they were expected to be warlike and aggressive until the age of sixty and then to go into retirement, look after the children and keep out of the way. But in general, as regards adult status, a whole series of dichotomies could be set up describing personality types who could adjust to such a culture with ease.

Side by side with this approach went a study of the tribal techniques of child rearing. Today the psychoanalysts are perhaps less certain about this matter than they were ten or fifteen years ago, when it was generally believed that there were certain childhood experiences whose effects could be detected in particular neurotic situations which repeated themselves again and again. One child, for example, had an exaggerated form of the oedipus, while another child felt himself rejected and consequently evolved certain assumptions about his own unworthiness.

Next, Kardiner and I tried to correlate insights arising from our attempt to deduct the type of personality that would fit into a given culture with data bearing on techniques of child care characteristic of that society. We soon found that there seemed to be a very considerable and meaningful correlation between the two. This finding was of great importance, since techniques of child care vary considerably from group to group. To take only one example, there are perhaps a dozen ways of carrying a child around: swaddled—tied to a cradle board—inside the mother's dress on her back, etc. I venture to say that each of these techniques of carrying the child around also has its own functional concommitants. For example—to take an obvious matter—if the child is carried around in the back of its mother's dress, this will provide a strong incentive indeed to toilet train the baby at an exceedingly early age. Thus I discovered that the Malagasy, who use this means of infant transportation, were able to have their children, one could hardly say "housebroken," it was more nearly "backbroken," by the age of six months. An infant of three or four months who fouled its mother would be seriously beaten and soon learned not to repeat the offense.

This, of course, could be expected to leave serious anal fixations and I think that the Malagasy character can, with no more than the usual stretch of the imagination, be made to show such anal traits. However, the most peculiar thing in regard to this is that the Malagasy are the only native people with whom I ever worked who had no laxative in their *materia medica.* They suffered severely from constipation, especially in times of anxiety, and have been known to die from autointoxication. This would be one of the simple, direct linkages between child training and basic personality which one does get now and then. I know of no other case in which this nexus expresses itself through quite such a beautiful and unmistakable correlation. It might be added that the Malagasy character, not unexpectedly, is docile and lacking in initiative and aggression.

To take another example, there are great differences between cultures in methods of child feeding: it can be fed whenever it squalls, fed on schedule, or fed when it is convenient for the mother to do so. The feeding itself may be a pleasurable process accompanied by cuddling and fondling or the child may be hurried along impatiently. It may be nursed at the breast or fed in some other manner. For instance, Marquesan women rarely nursed their children, since, in this society, the main function of the women was a sexual one, designed to keep as many hus-

bands as possible interested and happy. Since shapely
breasts were highly important in erotic play and attraction,
the women did not want to spoil them by nursing infants.
Instead, they fed the children on a mixture of pounded
breadfruit and coconut milk. I myself witnessed this
feeding process, which consisted in laying the child on its
back on a flat stone, taking a handful of this mixture,
holding it above the child's face and letting it trickle down
on the child's mouth. The child would sputter and gasp
and swallow as much of the mixture as it could. The
mother then wiped off the child's face with the edge of
her hand, took another handful and poured it on, and this
process was repeated until the child was fed. One can
easily imagine the feeling of these children toward their
parents! This method of feeding was certainly not con-
ducive toward developing a lot of affection and warmth,
particularly toward the mothers.

In brief, if we study culturally characteristic patterns of
child care as a whole, we are led to conclude that they
tend to produce personality types which would feel at
home in the type of society and culture in which such
child training patterns prevail. In other words, basic
personality types may be thought of as the products of
culturally characteristic childhood experiences. The adult
basic personality characteristic of a given society will—as
stated before—subsequently determine what new elements
can develop within that culture, and what new elements,
which reach the group through cultural diffusion, will be
found acceptable and will therefore be integrated into the
culture of that tribe.

(In this connection it is desirable to recall also what
was said somewhat earlier regarding the nexus between

the influence of objectively definable and describable training techniques and the emotional attitudes which accompany them. The Marquesan example is a particularly good illustration of the thesis that maternal attitudes have as much to do with character formation as have techniques. Indeed, the feeding of pap to the Marquesan child is emotionally not comparable to a feeding method which a primitive woman, belonging to a tribe where breast feeding is taken for granted, may improvise and resort to if her milk supply fails. The Marquesan technique is a direct expression of maternal rejection, and of the woman's tendency to define herself as a sexual rather than as a maternal person. [*Ed.*]

Once we managed to establish a correlation between child rearing techniques and the type of basic personality which would most readily feel at home in a given culture, we attempted to supplement our findings and constructs with a series of projective tests and life histories.

The Rorschach test was found to be particularly effective in cross cultural studies, and a high degree of correlation was found between the results of these tests and cultural studies. This does not mean, however, that Rorschach test results can wholly replace material obtainable through conventional anthropological studies of culture. There are a good many data, important for the understanding of the basic personality and even for the correct interpretation of Rorschach tests, which have to be obtained through a systematic study of culture.

The following example will illustrate this. Kwakiutl Indians, on being given the Rorschach test, gave fairly consistently answers of the following type: "This is a man (or a woman) cut in two" instead of saying: "two men," "or two women," which would be the usual answer. Such responses would, needless to say, strike the ordinary occidental Rorschach interpreter as manifestations of terrific aggression and hostility. However, in order to appraise correctly the meaning of such responses when given by Kwakiutl Indians, we must remember that whenever the Kwakiutl wanted to represent an entire animal on a flat surface, which provided no facilities for handling matters of perspective, they achieved this by splitting the animal down its back, and representing one half of the animal on each side of the center line, often with a common head in the middle. This, however, is still not the whole story, since we happen to know that the Kwakiutl are, indeed, a highly aggressive people. The question is, then, the following: does this art of theirs reflect the Kwakiutl Indian's suppressed aggressions and hostilities, or is it something that has arisen simply from the nature of their technology, with no particular reference to their psychology and to their hostilities. This is a point which has a great deal of importance for the proper interpretation of the "person split in half" response which they give to the Rorschach cards.

One thing that became evident from all Rorschach studies is that people do not see the ink blots as objects *per se;* they see *pictures* of objects. This implies that the conventions of artistic representation to which members of a society are accustomed influence their response to the Rorschach cards quite heavily, and therefore have to be taken into account in interpretation of Rorschach results.

Similar insights result from Rorschachs which were administered to Chinese subjects, who interpreted an amazing number of cards as landscapes. The ink blot pictures, turned sidewise, do resemble the typical Chinese landscape with the hills and trees reflected in a lake or pond, so that the interpretation was modified here also by the artistic conventions of the subject. These examples seem to indicate that the Rorschach tests, in spite of their lack of objectivity, cannot be used across cultural lines without loss of interpretative certainty through conventional interpretation techniques.

The Thematic Apperception tests, in which pictures tell a story, suggest a general plot or a personal relationship to a subject in any culture. However, the European subject receives a whole set of subtle clues, enabling him, e.g., to judge the social status of the pictured individuals from the costumes they wear, etc., which would be entirely lost on the non-European. Also, the TAT cards depict all sorts of situations that are characteristic or typical of the European life cycle, which a native just doesn't "get." For example, there is the TAT picture of a woman lying on a cot with her breasts bared, while a man stands beside her, apparently in great anguish, his arm across his face. A Navaho Indian, a fairly sophisticated young man who was working toward a Ph.D in anthropology at the University of New Mexico, volunteered for a TAT test. On being shown this card he said that this man, returning unexpectedly from college, had found his mother-in-law, who was visiting his wife, asleep in his room. He had entered quietly and had lit the lamp before he discovered this state of affairs and was now covering his eyes so that he should not go blind from looking at his mother-in-law— an act strongly tabooed in Navaho culture.

Another TAT card shows a figure cowering on a ledge with flying creatures overhead. An Alorese interpreted the evident distress of the pictured lad as arising from the fact that he had found a cave full of bats but had forgotten to bring his sling-shot and was therefore missing a good dinner. Bats to the protein-starved Alorese have an entirely different significance than to an American child brought up on the Halloween tradition.

I do not know how the person who administered these tests interpreted these answers, but to me they suggest that no really meaningful interpretation of TAT cards is possible without taking into consideration the cultural aspects of both the test material and the answers. Projective tests are useful in culture and personality studies, provided such cultural elements are taken into account.

In our study, data derived from projective tests were supplemented, whenever possible, by personal documents and particularly by autobiographies, life histories and the like. I can assure you that getting in a life history the material one wants for psychological purposes, without suggesting to the individual what to say, is a first class job. It is almost like psychoanalytic anamnesis to try to dig up early episodes which often have sunk into the subject's unconscious. Yet these are the sort of things that one would like to know.

One of the first conclusions we came to in this work was that, once again, we needed a lot more field work and a lot more information. However, after much additional data were gathered, we had quite clear indications of the existence of a wide-spread basic personality type in each of the societies we had worked with. As regards individual personality types, I would conclude that, given a large enough population, so that on a chance basis one might expect to get anything, one could probably duplicate in every society any personality configuration that can be found in any other society. However, the relative frequencies of the different personality types would vary enormously from society to society. One would find, for example, that a certain personality configuration which was so rare in one society that it would be regarded as psychopathological, might be the norm (in terms of showing the greatest relative frequency) in another society.

For instance, to take a simple example, the average Comanche man was very much the sort of person one could expect Comanche culture to produce. Of course in every culture there are "saints," who come closer to living according to the ideal patterns of the group than the normal individual ever does. Thus, there was an occasional Comanche who spent all his time on the warpath and got most of his satisfaction from killing people. But even the average Comanche was a thoroughly aggressive, self-reliant individual, because as a child he was subjected to a steady build-up, in which at each stage of his development he was given tests which were within his ability. The Comanche were careful never to expose the children to disappointment through failure, to reward them steadily for success in their tests and never to make them feel rejected or inadequate in any way. The result of this training was a curious lack of fear. For instance, I remember asking one of my older informants, "What did you use to do to purify yourself after you killed an enemy?" (Purification rites to prevent the ghost of the victim from coming back and working evil against his slayer are widespread, in Africa, in the Pacific Islands and also among the Comanche's neighbors, the Yuma and Pima.) The Comanche, however, looked blank and said, "Why should I be afraid of his ghost if I could kill him when he was alive?" This attitude pervaded the whole

Comanche way of life and, as a result, they were highly successful people. Interestingly enough, this attitude carried over into an almost complete indifference to survival after death and expressed itself in an almost complete lack of mythology concerning future life: and this in a people where it was taken for granted that most males would be killed before reaching the age of forty. The ideal career for a man was to accumulate a tremendous war record, reach the top in this competition and then be killed in battle and escape the humiliations of old age. As one of the Comanche war songs puts it, "It is pleasant to see young men's skulls. Their teeth are strong and white. Only young men's skulls laugh at the sun." Comanche training produced a particular kind of competitive, aggressive personality.

A man with Comanche characteristics would be completely lost in a group like the Zuni. His society would have no place for him and he would very probably be regarded as a witch and eliminated. Conversely, the docile, ritually controlled, unemotional individual, who is the Hopi or Zuni ideal, would be completely out of place in Comanche society—a deviant who would be regarded as psychopathological. In fact, many of the Plains tribes had an "out" for such men. They were allowed to assume the *berdache* role; that is, they became women, assumed women's dress, took part in women's activities, etc. However, this role did not exist in Comanche society; the man who couldn't be a warrior in this tribe was "sunk."

In brief, we have everywhere the full range of possible individual personality types, but always with different frequencies. This finding seems to indicate that there is a genuine correlation between patterns of child training and the sort of personalities which are typical of that society.

Another highly interesting point is the following. In several—though not in all—cases where we had life histories of primitive deviants, it was possible to understand that the culturally atypical early childhood experiences of these individuals caused them to become deviants. A very interesting case history of this type was recorded from the Alorese. In this tribe, the rule is almost complete parental neglect, and there are scarcely any friendly relations between parent and child, especially between father and child. In this tribe the adults deceive the children, use them to work off aggressions which are otherwise suppressed, etc. One of the results of this parental attitude is that the normal Alorese has no superego. He is simply afraid of being caught, but he never has any sense of sin whatsoever. There was only one man among those whom DuBois (19) studied who really seemed to have what one could call a conscience, and who was made uncomfortable by things he had done, even though he didn't think intellectually that he was going to be caught. Significantly, this man happened to be the son of a widower, whose behavior had been culturally atypical. This man's father had actually taken care of his child, had punished him, disciplined him, etc., but, by and large, had done all this justly and fairly. This educational pattern, which deviated from the Alorese norm, apparently led to the establishment of an emotional type which most of the Alorese didn't have. Material of this sort certainly tends to lend strong support to the thesis, most systematically propounded by Devereux (15), that the truly critical childhood experiences which make for deviation from the norm, both on the positive and on the negative side, are those which are *not* typical of the society and culture to which the child belongs.

As I see it, the factors that influence the formation of the personality operate through a variety of different levels. The first of these is the influence which culture exerts on the child, through the simple fact that other individuals—behaving in general in culturally patterned and culturally directed terms—act upon the child. We must remember that these influences operate on the child from birth, and continue to operate on him for a long period of time and *at* a time when the child's perceptive capacities, etc., are still of so exceedingly rudimentary a sort that it cannot differentiate between the reasons behind the things that happen to him. And one of these "things that happen to him" is precisely the technique of infant training which I mentioned previously. Now apparently, this early experience cannot be correlated, *item for item*, with anything in the later personality of the child. One cannot say that if the child is weaned at four months he will have such and such other adult characteristics. The same is true also of the date at which toilet training takes place. But what we can observe, and what is significant, is the *general atmosphere* in which the child is raised, and which may be permissive, affectionate, indifferent, hostile or whatnot. It is this atmosphere which establishes a definite series of anticipations in the child, which later will influence the manner in which he will register and experience all new situations that arise. In other words, he will see all new experiences in a manner determined by this series of anticipations, which goes back to his childhood. For example, a child who has been rejected or abused by his father will not have to go back *consciously* to his early memories when he encounters anyone in authority later in life; he will automatically interpret this situation in terms of his early father-child relationship experiences. I hardly need to add that he will enter such relationships with a chip on his shoulder, and will therefore almost certainly create a situation which will reinforce his anticipation as to what superiors are "really" like. What we have here is what I have called a series of highly generalized "responses in anticipation." You can also phrase it another way, and speak of anticipations resulting in certain types of response.

In addition, at a very early age the child also begins to learn concrete patterns of behavior. This learning is acquired partly through instruction. However, anyone who knows young children at first hand will recognize that a great deal of learning is the result also of imitation. It is surprising at how early an age a child will begin to imitate, and how much he will imitate. There is also an additional and very important factor which is operative at this point. Parents, I believe, tend to exaggerate the amount of *conscious teaching*, particularly of attitudes, that *they* can provide for their children. The child learns a great many of his responses and a great many of his patterns of behavior from other children, who are immediately above him in the age scale. In a very real sense, the adult is too far away, and his goals are therefore often so different from those accessible to the child that they are incomprehensible to him. I don't know whether many people nowadays read the Mary Poppins books, which are great favorites of mine. In one of them the children were told that when their father went away, he went down into the city and made money to support the family, and the children had a very clear picture of him "making it" on an anvil, with a sledge hammer.

The small children can't understand what the adults are trying to do much of the time, but they can understand perfectly well what a child who is only slightly older than they are is trying to do, and therefore they can and do model their behavior on him.

Another thing that is relevant in connection with the learning period is that, as Devereux stressed, the child learns at a surprisingly early age to contrast the sort of treatment *he* is getting with the sort of treatment *other* children are getting. This is a "joker," which again and again interferes with our getting a one-to-one relationship between an objective pattern of child treatment and the effect it has on the personality. For instance, in 18th century England, or New England for that matter, boys were thrashed regularly by their fathers for any offense or infringement of discipline. There was also an old English custom, called "beating the bounds," in which a villager would take the boys once a year around the bounds of the village territory and at each point marker give the boys a thrashing so that the boundaries would be impressed on their memories, enabling them later on to recall clearly the limits of the territory. Also, when a boy's father introduced him to someone important, he would knock him down at the important man's feet, saying, "Now, you'll remember this." The effect of such treatment on the personality was obviously tempered by the culture pattern. Since the same thing was happening to all the boy's contemporaries, its effect on personality formation was very different from what would result today if a father in our society treated his son in this way. The modern child would have a feeling of complete rejection and unworthiness and a deep feeling of resentment. Hence, in appraising the effect of a given child training technique on the personality, one must always take into account what the *individual* treatment means *relative* to the culturally determined treatment which *most other members* of the society are getting.

As the individual grows older his culture continues to exert influence on his personality by means of the particular forms of behavior which it requires of him, the things it rewards and the things it discourages. The problem here—and it is still an unsolved problem and one of the utmost importance to therapy—is how far these later experiences can actually alter the *fundamental* personality configuration. This is something we know little about. I would suspect that there is a considerable range of individual differences in susceptibility to a modification of the fundamental personality configuration by such later experiences. Certainly there appear to be differences at the child level.

Plant, in a book horribly mistitled *Personality and the Culture Pattern* (53), presents some material along this line, based on his observation of a long series of children. For example, he speaks of what he calls the "weathervane personality"; the child who will immediately respond to any external influence. Plant contrasts this with the child whose personality configuration is set like concrete at the age of five. This latter type of child may make realistic adaptations in his behavior as he grows older, but without fundamental changes so far as the *deeper* levels of his personality are concerned.

One more comment is in order before leaving the subject of the basic personality. While this concept is valid for small and relatively homogeneous groups of the sort which we have studied in our work, attempts to transfer this concept to large modern nations involve a very large step indeed and bring up the difference between "basic personality" and "national character." I recognize that any national group has a number of culture patterns in common. However, it is a big question how far we can go beyond simply stating that such groups have a community in overt behavior. No one has used the technique of random sampling, covering a range of localities, social classes, etc., and applied personality tests, to discover whether or not there are actually differences which set one nation apart from another. A modern nation is, after all, a more or less accidental aggregate of different local groups and social classes. Much has been done recently in trying to outline the "American character," notably by Margaret Mead (48) and Geoffrey Gorer (23). Americans have had a better chance of being homogenous than almost any other large national group, in spite of their diverse origins. The public school is a great leveler and the notorious desire for conformity evidenced by the offspring of most immigrant groups reinforces the trend toward uniformity. In addition, in most parts of America spatial mobility has been so high that we have not had groups settling down to develop local sub-cultures. By contrast, in the comparatively small territory of Great Britain, there are the Welsh, the Scots, the Irish and the English groups which originally spoke four different languages and which still cling to the old language or speak a thick dialect. They have, to be sure, taken over much of the common modern mechanized culture, but their value systems, patterns of behavior, and so on, differ profoundly at many points. The situation is further complicated by a class structure, which, although there is considerable social mobility nowadays, is still inherently rigid because of the existence of definite class-linked patterns of behavior, exemplified by the fact that the aristocrat is not supposed to display emotion under any circumstances.

An investigator taking random samples of personalities from each of these groups would undoubtedly get a different norm for each local division, and in many cases for each class group within the division. You may say that Great Britain is unusually diversified, but the French, for instance, present a similar problem. There are the Bretons, who don't even speak French, the Normans, famous for their attachment to hard liquor and for other Nordic characteristics, the French of the Midi in whom the Mediterranean emotional patterns are highly developed, etc. Even such small enclaves as the Norwegians and the Swedes insist, perhaps with more vehemence than the situation really calls for, that their nation includes all sorts of people—that the inhabitants of one Dahl are markedly different from the inhabitants of the next one in their behavior and their fundamental personality characteristics. It all comes down to the fact that members of a particular nationality behave alike at a number of points and a knowledge of this makes dealing with them more convenient. However, until we have much more *actual* psychological information on large European groups than we have now, it is exceedingly unwise and also unnecessary to talk about "national character." It is much safer to handle these observed similarities in terms of culture, to say that people act in such and such a way, without trying to imply that this indicates the existence of a distinct personality norm in the nation as a whole. It would no doubt be interesting to acquire data on this personality norm, if any, but I suspect that there would probably be so little in common between the personality norms of these different groups that the common element would not be much greater than we might find in all Europeans as contrasted with all West Africans.*

STATUS, ROLE AND STATUS PERSONALITY

In the preceding section, I discussed the problem of the influence which the culture pattern exerts on the personality of the members of the society whose culture is characterized by that pattern. In the concluding portions of that section I emphasized my doubts regarding the application of the broad concept of "basic personality" to large modern nations and stressed personality variations related to locality, social class and the like. This section's purpose is to refine these insights further by discussing the influence of social status and role upon the personality of those occupying certain statuses in society.

Status and role, as I use these concepts, were first defined in my book *The Study of Man* (*41*). A *status*, in the abstract, is a position in a particular pattern. The status of an individual represents his position in relation to his total society. Thus, the status of Dr. Brown as a member of society derives from a combination of all the

---

* Cf. the editor's review of A. Kardiner and R. Linton: *The Individual and His Society, Character and Personality* (*13*) for what is probably the first statement that the "basic personality" concept may not be operationally useful in the study of "national character." [*Ed.*]

statuses he holds: as a physician, as a Mason, as a Presbyterian, and as Mrs. Brown's husband and Johnny Brown's father. A *role* represents the dynamic aspect of a status. The individual is socially assigned to a status and occupies it with relation to other statuses. When he puts the rights and duties which constitute that status into effect, he is performing a role. Role and status are quite inseparable and the distinction between them is of merely academic interest. These concepts are simply tools, which facilitate the description of the structure of societies and help one to describe the participation of different groups of individuals in the culture.

One must remember that, in spite of the attempt to ascribe everything to society and social structure, the structure of a society is actually an aspect of its culture, consisting of the various behavior patterns, attitudes, etc., which are assigned to individuals occupying different positions within the social structure. One might say that the social system of a society is that part of its culture which provides adequate patterns for the interaction of the individuals, in the same way that another set of culture patterns provides adequate ways of exploiting the natural environment or of protecting the group from outside aggression. The mere fact of social living creates a whole series of problems which have to be solved in one way or another. The solution of these problems, by a process of trial and error, leads to the development of adequate patterns of behavior, which are then passed on from generation to generation, as a part of culture.

I would also like, at this point, to take exception to one widely disseminated view of society, which can be traced to certain of our own highly ethnocentric attitudes. There is a tendency, which began with Durkheim, but which is continued by the English functional school, to regard societies as desperately trying to hold themselves together through the development of various patterns of internal organization. It is understandable that such a view should be developed by those whose background has been an urban one, because the anonymous individuals who compose the population of the modern city are usually trying frantically to achieve some sort of organization and to develop some sort of common values and interests which will weld them into a functioning unit. However, this is a definitely anomalous situation and stems from the fact, not sufficiently recognized by social scientists, that cities can never "keep themselves going" by the simple process of breeding, so that their populations are made up to a considerable extent of adult strangers of mixed backgrounds, who have come together and have to find some way of getting along together.

Actually the normal human society is made up of individuals who are held together by such long patterns of association—be it by affection or by long established hostilities which have reached the trench warfare stage—that the behavior of friend or enemy can be perfectly anticipated. Such normal societies are held together by all sorts of personal ties operating actually at a sub-cultural level. You may remember in this context that I already insisted on the fact that both societies and cultures are continua, in that they persist through time. In the normal society, individuals are born into the society, grow up together, and in due course die off and, if all goes well, are buried in the village graveyard, so that the continuity is complete, even to the point where the dead have a place in social organization (42). The normal society is made up of persons of both sexes and all ages, who share a common culture and produce offspring to whom this culture is transmitted. It is the continuity of this group of individuals, organized into a society, which makes possible the organization of the group in several different ways at the same time. For instance, to take a familiar example, in a society such as Yale University you find, first, that the persons who make up this society are normally grouped into "students" and "faculty." In this formal pattern there are four undergraduate classes, and the graduate students, who are in an intermediate category because, although they are still students, they are aspirants to faculty status and often engaged in part-time teaching. Side by side with this pattern would be an entirely different type of organization involving fraternities, honor societies, and club memberships, campus organizations, memberships in athletic teams, etc. This series of organizational systems exists simultaneously and the individual's position in one of these systems is not necessarily related to his position in any of the others.

Every social structure is based on a series of fundamental categories, the most important of which is age and sex. The usual number of age and sex categories is seven. The first is made up of *infants* of both sexes, since, at this age, sex is not socially important; then come *boy, girl, adult male, adult female, old man* and *old woman.* Additional categories may be added to this group of seven basic categories, the most frequent additions being *adolescent males* and *adolescent females.* However, not all societies have a distinct category for adolescents. On the whole, the best way to find out whether or not this particular age-group is recognized as distinct is to discover whether or not there is a name for it.   Our 18th century ancestors did have a definite name, "lad" and "lass."   However, with the rise of the factory system and of child labor, adult responsibilities and activities began to seep down to the adolescent level.   This led to the disappearance of the appropriate terms denoting adolescents as a group, so that "lad" and "lass" survive only as archaisms in poetry and in the speech of certain rural British communities.

By contrast, among the Polynesians the young people between the age of puberty and marriage formed a special group in society, called in Marquesas the *kaioi* and in Tahiti the *arioi*.   These young people wore a special costume and had particular duties and a definite position in the society.   The boys received some formal instruction during this period, such as training in crafts, while the girls were given instruction in the arts of sexual attraction. Priests drilled them in religious chants and genealogies. The *kaioi* were the entertainers of the tribe, and were called upon to dance and sing at all ceremonies and feasts.   They also went on tours, performing their dances in the villages of other friendly tribes, where they would be feasted and presented with gifts after the entertainment.   Except for taboos among siblings, complete sexual license was permitted among these young people.   The Marquesan adolescents were distinguished by extraordinary self-confidence and composure.

In our own society the adolescents are in an undefined and intermediate position in the social structure.   Part of the time they are treated as children, subject to parental discipline; part of the time they are expected to take on adult responsibilities.   This situation produces considerable confusion in the minds of the young and may, in part, account for the fact that our most specific term for this section of society is "juvenile delinquent."

Definite attitudes and behavior patterns are ascribed to each of the age-sex categories, although patterns required from various age categories were often quite inconsistent with one another. A good example of such inconsistences could be found not long ago in our own society, where the "good child" was supposed to be docile, obedient, non-aggressive, "seen and not heard;" while the "good man" was supposed to be ruthless and aggressive, building a fortune in a new country and getting as much as he could by any kind of piratical means. Another example of this sort of thing is the "jeune fille" in France, who is treated like a child and is expected to be docile, submissive and ignorant of the facts of life up to her wedding night. After marriage, she is suddenly expected to take on important directive functions and, in the "petite burgeoisie" at least, to administer the family income. One of the great puzzles for psychologists, and one which has not yet been adequately solved, is: How it is possible for the average individual to make these shifts without some sort of nervous breakdown? I say *average* individual, because certainly many people are faced with this in all societies and, while it may be the cause of more neuroses than we know at this point, most people are able to make the shift.

The reason maturing individuals are able to make these big shifts in behavior is due to the fact that in most societies the demands which are made on an individual as he passes from one age category to another are perfectly clear-cut. Hence the individual knows exactly how to behave under most circumstances. He knows what is childish behavior and what is adult behavior and consequently can operate in straight "reinforcement-extension" terms of learning. A particular age-group has no formal internal organization, but, given anything which touches its interests directly, such a group can frequently operate with considerable unity of purpose.

The second broad category of social structure contains family systems, which, in contrast with age-sex systems, do involve *internally organized* units. There is a family structure present in all societies. In every society we have what we call the nuclear family. This is a group of two or more adults of both sexes and the offspring. It is everywhere a unit for the production and consumption of goods, and is, above all, a unit for the raising of children. Then, beyond this, we have what we call "families," although it would be better if we had a different term for it, because it often includes various kin extensions. Such a "family" may run to a hundred or more relatives—and, by the way, this system is not limited to "primitives." One of my friends, who married a Brazilian girl of the upper class, told me that he never really appreciated what the term "extended family" meant, until he went to Rio de Janeiro and began to meet his wife's relatives. I myself stood as godfather to his son at what was only a small "family function," with only the closest relatives present—and there were one hundred and twenty-five of them. Of course, there are various ways by which one can delimit these kin groups, and, besides, I do not think that kin groups have an important role in our psychological discussion of personality formation. On the other hand the nuclear family very decidedly does play an important role in such investigations, because the nuclear family, or whatever its functional substitute for child rearing is, represents the closest and most continuous contacts which the child has with adults. It represents a situation or setting in which the particular interpretations given to the cultural patterns by the parents have a strong effect on the child. Hence, children reared in accordance with the same culture patterns, but in different families, actually do not have identical experiences, precisely because, as I have already explained, all culture patterns have a range of possible *variations*.

The third organizational fact is that there are, in every society, *associations*. These are voluntary groupings of individuals, based on congeniality or common interest. The functional importance of these associations varies considerably from society to society. In fact, there is a certain sort of balance here between the kin group and the association groupings. This was pointed out long ago by historians of law, who stressed that contractual obligations and contractual law tend to replace kin law as one rises in the scale of civilization; i.e., as one approximates more and more the Western European patterns. In cases where kinship ties are thoroughly extended, and where the kin group has numerous functions, associations may be comparatively weak, although there is a tendency in societies where the kin ties are strong enough or extended enough to emphasize individual friendships as a "way out" for the individual.

Two quotations come to mind in this context. One is from Bernard Shaw, to the effect that the universal regulation against incest, present in all societies, is based on a hearty natural aversion toward relatives. The other is:

"God gives us our relatives, but thank God we can chose our own friends." Apparently when one has a large number of relatives toward whom he has obligations of all kinds, one is badly in need of a friend. Under such circumstances there are likely to arise patterns of formal friendship. West African friendship patterns are described in an illuminating treatise on Dahomey by Herskovits (27). In this society everyone, even the king, had a best friend, to whom he confided his troubles in a Damon and Pythias arrangement. It did not imply quite everything that the Greek relationship implied, although a great devotion and absolute confidence were a part of such a relationship. The important thing about this type of association is that it is entered into voluntarily, so that the individual has a range of choice in selecting his comrade. Such associations extend all the way from simple friendship to work groups, trade relations and the like.

A fourth category found in every society is a system of occupations. All societies have a differentiation of activities and the assignment of particular skills, knowledge, and so on, to particular categories of individuals. For instance, the distinction between male and female activities is to be found in all societies, as an absolute minimum of occupational differentiation. This has some interesting connotations. For example, in a culture that is undergoing a rapid process of change, there may well be a period of uncertainty with regard to the proper place of a new occupation in the social scheme and the new occupation will not be assigned to one sex or the other until it becomes integrated into the society. In our own society we find that, since women will work for less money than men, as soon as women get into an occupation, the men get out of it. However, a sexual division of labor is a universal phenomenon, which can be found even in societies where the rewards for men and for women are exactly the same. Apparently, then, for whatever reason, any new occupation is eventually, though only after an initial period of uncertainty, assigned either to men or to women. There are some very interesting cases of this. For instance, telephone exchanges were originally staffed by men, because most mechanical things were considered in the province of the male in the early days of mechanization. However, perhaps because of certain characteristics of the feminine status personality, it soon became apparent that women were more patient and courteous with unreasonable clients, hence, men were completely replaced in this job by women. In the same way, a hundred years ago secretaries were always men. Nowadays, the term "secretary" evokes the picture not only of a woman, but of a pretty young woman with matrimony in view. Likewise "stenographer" connotes a young female, unless the reference is specifically to a court stenographer, who is almost invariably a man. Undoubtedly this tendency toward sex differentiation is simply a part of a broader tendency to differentiate occupations and assign them to different groups.

Of course, as the culture increases in complexity, a longer and longer time is required to learn the skills needed to carry on a particular occupation. We therefore find an increasing differentiation into definite occupational groups, as exemplified by the various professions and crafts among ourselves.

The last and exceedingly important structural category

to be mentioned is that in all societies we have not only individuals who compose the society as a whole, but also the various constituent groups, which are established by any and all of these systems of organization and which are arranged in a graded series which we may very well call "prestige series." Indeed there is no such thing as a truly equalitarian society and it seems highly improbable that there ever has been or will be one. The study of prestige is one which is likely to be very rewarding. Age and sex categories are in every society arranged in a series, usually with the *adult male* at the top—sometimes with the *old male*—but never, so far as I know, with the *adult female* at the top. This is true even for matriarchal societies. A matriarchal society is merely one in which the biological father cannot spank *his own* children, since the children are not considered to belong to his family. However, the maternal uncle, the mother's brother, is in a position to spank them and also probably ready to spank the woman herself, since he has the relevant rights and privileges of a husband in patriarchal societies. In brief, the normal high points in this age-sex series is the male.

In any community the families also are arranged in a graded series, the basis for this varying from one society to another. These reasons may include all sorts of factors, such as wealth, birth, the part of town the family lives in, special abilities, or anything of the kind. But, whatever the actual criteria may be in a given society, there is in every society a certain series of criteria which is recognized as giving prestige. There is one simple way of determining where a particular family stands in this prestige series. All one has to do is find out which families are willing to intermarry with this family, and which families *they* would like to intermarry with. This is one of the areas where prestige differences come out immediately and strongly.

Similarly, among association groups there are always certain work groups, clubs, etc. which are "better" than others. Some occupations are likewise regarded as more honorable than others.

The position or positions of the individual within these systems are referred to as his status. This term, unless qualified, refers to positions observed at a particular point in time. The term "status" ordinarily carries with it the connotation of "a place in a prestige series." As a matter of fact, however, even in nonsociological usage, one may speak of the "status of adolescent," for instance when an adolescent boy is brought into court. Hence, this term means simply "the position of the individual."

This set of positions or statuses serves as a guide for the conscious training of young individuals. There are two general types of status, which can be distinguished and which I have originally called the "ascribed" status and the "achieved," (*41*) although I now prefer to denote the latter by the term "acquired status." "Ascribed" statuses are those which can be predicted for an individual from the moment of birth. As soon as the doctor announces, "It's a boy," you can be fairly sure that this infant will become a husband and father, that he will have to learn an occupation of some sort, that, in the present world, he will have to do at least 18 months of military service, and a few other things of the kind. Consequently, since it is known what the goals of his training are, it is possible to work on the boy from infancy and to shape him to the particular psychological and behavioral patterns which will fit him for the successful occupation of these statuses. This is socially very important, since the ascribed statuses take care of most of the business of living in any society and insure that the sort of things which have to be done, to keep the society functioning and to secure its survival, are done.

However, there are also, in all societies, certain "acquired statuses," i.e., posts which have to be filled and which can't be filled by "just anybody." For instance, no amount of formal training can make anybody into a successful general, or into a good dancer or a good poet, or into an industrial organizer of the type of Henry Ford. Hence, there are in every society certain positions, largely connected with occupations and with leadership, which have to be left open to competition. Hence, the individuals who have the necessary ability are able to move into these statuses.

Finally, there are also what may be termed "negative statuses," such as that of the village drunkard, who was present in almost every community in my youth. This was definitely, as every reader of Mark Twain's *Huckleberry Finn* knows, an acquired status, which had its reputable functions.

In brief, a status is constructed by combining two sets of factors. First of all, there are,—and this is where the distinction between status and role comes in—certain prerequisites; that is, only individuals with certain characteristics, such as members of a certain age-sex group, or members of a certain social class, can occupy particular statuses. For instance, to be president of the United States, one must have been born in the United States and must be over thirty-five years old. Furthermore—although this is not stated in the Constitution—one has to be white and, for the present time at least, Protestant. In brief, it is possible to define, right from the start, the sort of person who can occupy this status. In every society there must be husbands and fathers and we assume that this status can be held only by adult males. However, there are large sections of Africa where it is not necessary to be an adult male to acquire this status. One of the highest goals in parts of Africa is to found a family with numerous wives and offspring, with all the consequent rewards of being a "pater familias" on earth and a devoutly worshiped ancestor after death. These rewards are of such importance, that when a woman becomes rich and important enough, she sets herself up as a "husband" and "father." She buys wives and loans them to gentlemen of her acquaintance for breeding purposes; the children refer to her as "father" and the wives address her as "husband." In this way she becomes the founder of a new lineage and is worshipped as the only ancestor. However, this is, of course, an atypical situation (58).

Thus, there are, first of all, the *prerequisites for status* and, second, the *behavior* which is prescribed for the occupants of a given status towards persons who occupy other statuses within that particular system. This behavior is called the "role." It is a collection of culture patterns which can be stated in terms of culture constructs, irrespective of the actual behavior of the various individuals who occupy the status and practice the roles. However, there is a tendency to use "role" to denote the individual's behavior in a particular status, rather than the culturally prescribed behavior pertaining to it. To meet this situation I now use, rather tentatively, the term "role interpretation," as one speaks of an actor's interpretation of a particular role. Again, I must remind you that the culture pattern (although it is expressed in terms of the mode of a range of variations) is actually a range of variations in behavior within which the behavior will be effective. Each individual, operating in the performance of his role, will, under ordinary circumstances, and at least in public, keep within the limits prescribed by the culture pattern. Nevertheless, as his interaction with a particular individual in another status is repeated, the role performance will be modified on both sides, until the two finally will work out a habitual reciprocal behavior, i.e., an adjustment of the two "role interpretations" to each other. A simple example of this is one's behavior toward a strange policeman. You know that there are certain things, largely unpleasant, which policemen *per se* are expected to do, and certain ways in which you are expected to react to them. Nevertheless, if a particular policemen has had his beat in your neighborhood for five or six years and you know him well and pass the time of day with him, the two of you will develop a different attitude and a different pattern of mutual response. These will be your respective "role interpretations."

Since in each society there are multiple systems of organization, each individual necessarily occupies a multiple status, although it is obvious that he cannot perform all of them simultaneously. Hence, an individual has at any point in time both active and latent statuses. The active status is the one in terms of which one is operating at the moment, or, in other words, the status whose role one is just then performing. One's latent statuses are those positions in the social system which one occupies and whose obligations, performances and so on one knows perfectly well, but in terms of which one is not acting *at this time*. This, by the way, can be extended to include even persons who are members of different societies, because the same person may have status in several different societies simultaneously. To cite a quite personal example, I have one status at Yale, but when I return to the Quaker community in which I was born and reared, I have an entirely different status. Hence, if I return there, I will be known as Isaiah Linton's son. The old people will greet me at a Quaker meeting and say "It is good to see thee back again. What is thee doing now?" "I am teaching at Yale," I reply. "Well, I hear it is a right good school," and there the matter ceases. Although my status there is very different from my status at Yale, when I am in the Quaker community I fall into its patterns and its speech and can operate perfectly well in its terms.

I can think of an even more extreme personal example. I haven't been in the Marquesas for thirty years, but I am sure that if I arrived there tomorrow, within twenty-four hours there would be a large collection of my native "relatives" seated on the front porch. The word would have been spread and I would be introduced to each one of them with the proper degree of relationship, since on my earlier sojourn there I was adopted into a family by a process based on the exchange of names. I exchanged names with a young man called Feo, which made him and myself "social equivalents," so that all his relatives were also my relatives. Hence, if I returned, every one of these adopted relatives would bring me a gift, appropriate to the degree of relationship which united us, and every one would expect a return gift, also appropriate to the degree of kinship, but somewhat larger than the one I received. Thus, I have status, with appropriate patterns of behavior, in three different societies.

The individual who is operating, shall we say, in his professional capacity as a doctor, is expected to follow definite forms of behavior. During consulting hours he performs as a doctor, and then, leaving his telephone number, he goes home where he proceeds to function as a husband and father. On Sunday he may also be a vestryman in a church. In any society certain statuses normally converge on the same individual. The roles have been adjusted by practice, so that there is no serious interference between them. However, in all societies there are occasions when, by unfortunate circumstance, the individual finds himself occupying two statuses whose roles are mutually incompatible. This situation provides the material for tragedy or breakdown, since the individual is torn between two sets of behavior which are in conflict.

The conflict of roles which comes from holding a double status is the underlying motive of the tragedy of the House of Oedipus, where, because of the accident of marriage, the individuals are united by double statuses and double roles which, by definition, are completely incompatible. For example, the mother is also the wife; the child is also the half-brother or half-sister of the father, and so on. As a result, a whole set of conflicting claims arise. Another familiar example of this is the old Scottish story, claimed by a number of clans as part of their clan history. A man who killed a clansman and knew he would be hung for the deed seeks shelter at the nearest house, a request which no Highlander could refuse without loss of face. The host then discovers that this man has killed his brother. In his capacity as brother, it is his duty to avenge the death by killing the murderer; on the other hand, as host, he must protect the man who has taken shelter beneath his roof. What happens in the legend is what usually happens in cases of incompatible roles: the individual acts in terms of one status at a time. The Scottish host protected the murderer from the other members of his clan, saw him safely across the clan border and then attacked him and fought him to the death.

The next point to be made is that the occupancy of a particular status usually involves not only the performance of *overt culture* patterns but also what may be called the covert elements of culture, that is, the particular attitudes, values, character attributes, and so on, which are attributed to individuals in this position. There are always ideal patterns of this sort, which are consciously stated for most statuses and which are congruous with the ideal patterns for role performance. For example, since the father is supposed to be just, though no longer stern, in our society, he must certainly maintain some dignity in dealing with the child; he is also supposed to be generous, within limits, and is expected to set up certain patterns for the child to follow. All this takes place within the family. When it comes to occupational groups and class groups in class organized societies, there may be very considerable differences in the personality characteristics of the members of that society. The same is true of sex differentiations. Among ourselves, women are supposed to be much gentler, kinder and more patient than males. However, among the Iroquois, exactly the opposite was the case. When the Iroquois wanted a good job of torturing done on a pet enemy, they turned him over to the women, who displayed more ingenuity and ruthlessness along this line than the men were capable of (35).

The Chinese situation is also interesting in this connection, because there, in regard to general personality characteristics, women and children are grouped together; that is, the Chinese woman is presumably viewed as a child who has never grown up. Different patterns of behavior are expected of the men, depending upon the class of society to which they belong and their varying occupations. The scholar and the official must not express emotion and must be courteous under all circumstances; the peasant is allowed to lose his temper and express his emotions violently—particularly verbally. I remember my friend E. A. Ross telling me that, when he was in China, he heard two coolies indulging in a most violent altercation. It went on and on, until Ross said to his Chinese friend, "Why don't they fight?" The friend said, "You don't understand; The one that strikes the first blow confesses that he has run out of ideas."

In formulating the ideal patterns for role performance, culture provides us with means for an anticipation of the individual's behavior which is congruous with the formal patterns of role behavior. The chief question in every case is how these patterns coincide with the *reality of the individual's character*. Before we may judge this, we must try to find out by informal methods, other than projective tests, what the person's character is. This we can do by seeking to understand what role he is performing at a given time. Sociologists are familiar with the inter-action studies of Elliott Chapple (7). I once asked Dr. Chapple what the origination rate of a magistrate, trying to settle a parking ticket, was. Since the origination rate is determined by how much talking you do and how much you "start," the magistrate's rate would be exceedingly low. Thus, one must figure that the statuses and roles are involved in human action. An amazing "front" can be developed by people, particularly in the case of members of different classes within the same society. Anyone who is familiar with Southern Negroes knows that there is a very definite form of role behavior which the Southern Negro normally adopts in dealing with Whites. He is supposed to be cowardly, ridiculous and stupid and, if he acts in this way, he is rewarded for it (*18*). Thus, the individual who "plays stupid" can get out of all sorts of responsibilities and work. It is only when one actually gets to know individuals in this group well enough to get behind this "role façade" that one realizes what sort of personality one is really dealing with. It seems to me that the problem for the psychologist here is to try to find out *how far the personality norms of various status groups within a society actually correspond to the assumed stereotypes for these.* This is something about which we know very little. I think that we do have indications that, in small homogeneous societies, there exist certain personality norms which differ from one society to another. Presumably these "status personalities," as I have called them, would represent such personality norms plus or minus certain factors related to the status the individual holds. Such a study may seem simple, but is actually exceedingly difficult, because we don't really know much about this field, which deserves more study. The study of age and sex series, in particular, presents interesting problems as does the study of individuals who seem to change their personalities as they move from one status to another in a series. Thus, all societies recognize the sobering effects of having to assume certain types of responsibility. An individual who has been wild may very well change and become a responsible man and a good leader if a suitable task is assigned to him. Again, we have to go back to the problem of how extensive, and particularly how deep running, are the changes in personality which are connected with the changes in overt behavior and also with the changes in the demands which the society makes on the individual. This has a great bearing on the whole problem of normality and abnormality, particularly as regards the problem of how far psychotherapy can modify the basic personality structure of the adult patient.

Under such circumstances the problem of what constitutes normality becomes quite complicated. It seems that one must distinguish between absolute and relative abnormality. All societies provide examples of psychotics, neurotics, and hysterics, who are recognized as such by the members of that society. The symptomatologies associated with these abnormal states differ from society to society in ways which strongly suggest that they are shaped by cultural influences. The methods employed by different societies in dealing with individuals of these different types, including the social utilization of certain forms of psychic abnormality, also differ. However, it seems certain that abnormality of this sort is absolute and probably has a physiological basis. Individuals having the constitutional defects responsible for such abnormalities would be abnormal in any society. At most, particular cultural factors may lead to the manifestation or suppression of symptoms at various levels of defect intensity.

Relative normality, on the other hand, is a matter of the individual's adjustment to the cultural milieu and of the degree to which his personality configuration approaches the basic personality of his society. Tests, supplemented by life histories, analytic studies, etc., have shown that, when the individual deviates widely from the basic personality, his early experience has frequently been atypical for his society (*15, 19*).

The tests of absolute normalcy are the individual's ability to apprehend reality, as understood by his society, to act in terms of this reality, and to be effectively shaped by his society during his developmental period. The test of relative normalcy is the extent to which the individual's experience has given him a personality conforming to the basic personality of his society.

II

Cultural Influences in Neurosis and Psychosis

EXAMPLES OF PRIMITIVE PSYCHOSES

Because of the profound differences involved, the study of psychoses in non-European societies would be of great value to psychiatric theory. Unfortunately, data are meager and incomplete. It is impossible even to determine the frequency of psychoses in most of these societies, for a variety of reasons, which we will examine more closely anon, and which include such factors as the lack of public facilities for the care of the insane, the concealment of insanity by families who view it as a disgrace, and the fact that in many societies the "missing soul hypothesis"—to be discussed in detail in connection with hysteria, in Chapter III—provides a satisfactory sanction for killing the troublesome psychotic.

Before I go further into the matter of what data are available regarding the incidence of mental disorder in general and the relative incidence of various types of psychosis in particular, I would like to take a moment to underscore the importance and interest of studies of this type by discussing briefly two forms of mental disorders which are apparently highly localized. These are the disorders known as *Witigo* and *Koro*.

Witigo (*Witiko, Windigo*) (8, 24, 25, 37). A fairly
clearly localized psychosis of great cultural interest is the
Witigo cannibalistic insanity of some of the Canadian
Indians, such as the Chippewa and the Cree tribes. Actually the word *witigo* has two meanings. On the mytho-
logical level it is the name of a cannibalistic monster or
demon, which lives as an ice skeleton in winter and dies
each spring, only to revive again with the coming of cold
weather. Some tribes believe that this ice skeleton monster also has a heart of ice. It is greatly dreaded, since it
haunts settlements and devours human beings. In a sense,
this monster is the epitomy of the dread winter season with
all it implies for men in terms of suffering, starvation and
loneliness. Indeed, in winter the scarcity of game obliges
each family to live on its own hunting territory, many miles
from the next family, and to rely entirely upon game which
is often hard to find. During these terrible winters many
human beings perish from starvation, and cases of cannibalism—which, due to isolation, are almost always *intra-
familial* ones—were known to occur. Thus, this cannibalistic demon symbolizes both the climax of human misery and
despair, and the last and most dreaded expedient one may
resort to during famine: endocannibalism. The starving
Indians' temptation to commit cannibalism must be extreme indeed to have led them to evolve the notion that
cannibalism is the most horrible deed anyone can possibly
perform and that the cannibalistic person himself is a kind
of demon or monster.

Indeed, the second meaning of the term *witigo* is a human being who has cannibalistic desires and often actually
becomes a man eater. There are many ultimate causes assigned by the natives for the transformation of a person

into a human *witigo:* malicious witchcraft, the person's own attempts to become a protégé of the *Witigo* demons, etc. As a rule, the onset of the *witigo* condition is marked by an acute depression, sometimes involving lethargy, with pronounced anxiety over possible starvation . . . perhaps as a result of the evil machinations of a hostile witch. The ailing person gradually begins to see the members of his family as fat, appetizing beavers and becomes aware of his urge to devour them. Sometimes—in lucid moments—he may realize the pathological nature of this impulse and may therefore even beg others to kill him, lest he should turn into a cannibal. In other cases—many of which are well documented and entirely beyond doubt—the acute depression gradually lifts and the patient becomes a cannibal, who, after devouring his own family—sometimes in the most coldblooded and seemingly calm manner—begins to seek also other human prey.

It is believed that during the early stages of the illness the cannibalistic impulse can be cured. There are stories of the patient being made to vomit the heart of ice which is forming within him, and which is then burned. Other types of shamanistic cures are also on record. However, once cannibalism has become an actuality, the human *witigo* is doomed by his fellow men, who not only kill him, but burn his corpse to cinders, in order to melt the hidden ice which forms part of the human *witigo's* anatomy, and which corresponds to the ice skeleton of the demon *Witigo.*

The above is but a rough sketch of what seems to be the common denominator of the *witigo* psychosis in several Canadian Indian tribes. It suffices, however, to enable us to stress the cultural basis of this particular form of psychosis, since no such cannibalistic psychoses, correlated with mythology, and with demons, seem to exist in other areas among subarctic tribes, many of whom certainly face cold and starvation almost as often as do the hunting Canadian Indians. Thus, whereas hunger and ice are ever present threats also in other areas, this particular psychotic *phrasing* of the manifestations of ultimate despair is a distinctively localized and cultural phenomenon, closely correlated with many aspects of Chippewa mythology, shamanism, social organization, economy and habitat.

Koro. Another very interesting type of culturally localized derangement is *Koro,* which seems to occur only in Southeastern Asia, and particularly among the inhabitants of the Malay Archipelago and among those Southern Chinese who have migrated to this region.* Van Wulfften Palthe (62), whose account I summarize here, states that it seems particularly prevalent among the Buginese and Macassarese of Indonesia and that it is reported also from West Borneo. He knew personally a Chinese from Borneo, who had this illness.

Koro is a name given to an anxiety state in which the patient is afraid that his penis will withdraw into his abdomen, and that, as a result of this, he will die. This anxiety has a very sudden onset, is very intense and sometimes lasts for several days. In order to prevent the penis from disappearing into the abdomen, the patient holds it in a vise-like grip, and is assisted in this also by his wife, friends and relatives, since the penis may not be released even for an instant. In other instances the penis is lashed to some contrivance, the box in which native goldsmiths and Chinese apothecaries keep their scales being the preferred one.

---

* Its occurrence in Southern China proper (Fatshan, Kwantung) was reported by Fritz Kobler (36). [*Ed.*]

After long and weary hours of unremitting vigilance the anxiety wears off, but often recurs. Van Wulfften Palthe had occasion to observe this condition in a Chinese man hospitalized for tuberculosis, from whom he learned that the Chinese called this illness *shook yong*, meaning "penis shrinks," and that it can be cured according to the principles of ancient Chinese medicine, by giving medications representing the male or warm principle, to counteract the female or cold principle which predominates in this illness.

This anxiety is related to the belief that the corpse *has* no penis because it is held that it *could* not have one. Hence, a withdrawal of the penis into the abdomen—its disappearance—must, in their belief, be a token of impending death. This explains why small Chinese boys on the point of death have their penis sucked or have a little weight attached to it, to prevent its withdrawal into the abdomen.

Our authority on this illness correlates *koro* with castration anxiety and stresses that the one patient he could observe personally had been afraid of women all his life. He had never cohabited with one, and had masturbated instead, despite parental warnings that this would cause his penis to shrivel and to withdraw into the abdomen. In other words, his parents warned him against his bringing about the *shook yong* or *koro* illness by masturbating. This castration fear is, in turn, intimately related in native belief to the aforementioned fear of death since, despite the existence of Chinese eunuchs who had been deprived *both* of the penis and the testes, people firmly continue to believe that total castration results in death. This belief is so deeply ingrained in that area that even non-schizophrenics sometimes attempt suicide by cutting off their organs.

Van Wulfften Palthe distinguishes between two aspects of *koro*. On the one hand it is an imaginary organic illness, and, on the other hand, it is a very genuine anxiety state, which that author considers a neurosis but which, in accordance with the definition of psychosis which I give elsewhere (p. 81) I am inclined to label a psychosis.

As far as I know, this complex of beliefs concerning the retraction of the penis into the abdomen and the anxiety state which it elicits is limited to the Southeast Asiatic area, at least in the sense of a distinct clinical entity. This impression is materially strengthened by the fact that even a female equivalent of *koro* is known to occur in this area. Thus, in Borneo some female patients feel that their breasts are shriveling up and that their labia are being sucked inward, the whole amounting to a disappearance of female sex characteristics.*

The above examples of culturally and geographically localized psychoses clearly indicate the extent to which cultural beliefs can influence delusion and behavior in mental disorder.

THE ORGANIC SUBSTRATUM

Physiological factors cannot be ruled out in studies of personality development. However, they are so closely integrated with other elements in forming the frame within which personality develops, that here, as in the case of single experiential elements particularly, the same or closely similar physiological factors may result in different psychological configurations.

With respect to psychoses, the main problem at the pres-

---

* Occidental *koro* fantasy equivalents are also known to exist (17). [*Ed.*]

ent time would seem to be that of the genesis of various types. Work which has been recently carried on at Yale under my direction would seem to indicate that all the fundamental types of psychoses which are recognized by Europeans also occur in other societies, although the particular symptoms may differ considerably from one society to another. This would seem to suggest the existence of a genuine physiological bases for all psychoses. On the other hand, from the little we know at present of psychosomatics, it seems quite possible that predisposing physiological causes may become effective only in the presence of particular social and cultural conditions. High blood pressure, which apparently is the result of an inextricable mixture of physiological and psychological factors, would be a good example.

On the whole, I feel that the material which I am about to present suggests that some general pattern of damage to the nervous system underlies all forms of psychosis, though it is shaped in its expression by social and cultural factors.

In the present state of our knowledge, it certainly is proper for us to proceed most cautiously. Nonetheless, it seems to me that data regarding mental disorders in other societies tend to suggest that there is a definite, though often not easily detectable, foundation in the organic realm for whatever psychiatric illness may become manifest on the behavioral and verbal levels. This thesis is certainly not easy to demonstrate conclusively, but it is my considered opinion that considerable weight may be attached for example to Tooth's careful comparisons between trypanosomiasis—usually referred to as tryps for short—and schizophrenia. After stressing the general difficulties of diagnosing tryps, he specifically states that it is often not easy to differentiate between mental symptoms of tryps and of schizophrenia . . . adding the crucially important remark that "principal clinical varieties [of schizophrenia] are the same in Africans as in other races" (*60*, p. *6*).

He stresses the frequency of simple dementia in tryps patients, adding that where pathological sleeping is absent, there is little to differentiate it from schizophrenia, except in that it is less common in young people and is mostly seen in the terminal stages. The paranoid group is less common, and delusions are seldom systematized and endogenous; although mild paranoid reactions have been noted in the case of schoolboys. As regards the catatonic type, Tooth tells us that excitement with florid symptoms is common in tryps and difficult to distinguish from catatonic schizophrenia, particularly since there is often a marked incongruity of affect. There are also delusions which are often based on hallucinations, particularly of the auditory type. Unfortunately Tooth was unable—due to language problems—to establish whether or not the stream of talk in tryps definitely resembles the schizophrenic pattern, but he was able to ascertain that such patients often complain of "mixed thoughts." He also noted various dysphasias and suggests the possibility that what appears as thought disorder may be fundamentally a problem of dysphasia. True catatonic waxen flexibility was not observed, though stupors and mutism do occur.

Equally important is the presence in both disorders of physical signs attributable to vasomotor and endocrine disturbances. There are myxoedematous types, hyperthyroid types, persons who show the so-called "greasy skin" and patients with the moist, cold extremities and the expressionless face of the schizophrenic. Tooth specifies that "acute, schizophrenia-like psychoses are more often seen in persons of asthenic habitus, whereas the simple, dementing type of patient is more often pyknic or dysplastic" (*op. cit.* p. 7). I shall not dwell on the controversial point of testicular atrophy noted by some—but not generally accepted—both in tryps and in schizophrenia. By contrast, it seems well established that in both conditions the more sudden and stormy the onset, the better the prognosis.

This list of correspondences is certainly impressive, and I wish to stress again that we are not comparing here the clinical picture of tryps in the African and that of schizophrenia in the European, since Tooth specifically starts out by saying that all forms of schizophrenia observed in Europe and America are also found in the African. He feels, of course, that whereas the psychotic manifestations of tryps are secondary to brain changes, those of schizophrenia may be secondary to endocrine involvements. Be that as it may, in another context Tooth returns to this similarity, and stresses that in the "bush" people a typical schizophrenia picture is most likely to be due to organic illness, while schizophrenia proper appears as an amorphous, endogenous psychosis, since only in the urban and literate Negro does schizophrenia have nearly the same forms as in Europe.

The preceding data certainly suggest the possibility that schizophrenia may have an organic basis, since it is clear that a practically identical psychiatric picture may occur also in tryps, to the point of making a differential diagnosis sometimes quite difficult, at least on the basis of the strictly psychiatric symptomatology.

Another of Tooth's very thought provoking findings also points in the same direction. In the past, most writers have attached a great deal of importance to the loss of cultural and familiar connections in the causation of mental disorder. Thus, acculturation, or adaptation to the mode of life of the ruling alien, has been held responsible for an increase in psychosis as well as in neurosis. Tooth's data do not challenge the hypothesis that neuroticism in the literate African may be due to acculturation strains. However, the situation seems somewhat different regarding the psychoses commonly held to be "functional." Limiting his considerations to the non-organic psychoses, Tooth divides them—admittedly heuristically—into reactive and endogenous ones. He then stresses that if the acculturation-strain hypothesis were correct, one would have to expect among literates a higher proportion of reactive psychoses than of endogenous pyschoses. He also specifies that if one assumes that heredity factors are manifested in the fact that near relatives of the patient are also affected, one would expect a lower incidence of such hereditary factors among the literate than among the non-literate. However, his figures indicate that the difference between literates and non-literates having affected near relatives is negligible: 34.0% as against 40.9%. "Though psychogenic factors were found with greater frequency in those who did not show a hereditary taint, the difference was not significant, possibly because the numbers were so small" (*op. cit.*, p. 62). At any rate, Tooth concludes that "this survey provides no evidence in support of the hypothesis that psychosis is commoner in the Westernized group than in the rest of the population" (*op. cit.*, p. 62). He adds that the data of Cunyngham

Brown, obtained in Nigeria, also indicate the absence of a significant difference in regard to the incidence of supposedly non-organic psychoses in acculturated and unacculturated groups.

Tooth's data just cited, while not conclusive, do have considerable importance when taken in conjunction with his demonstration of the similarity between tryps psychoses and schizophrenias, and gain further plausibility from a third consideration.

I refer to the observation that whereas the concrete symptomatology of a given disorder may vary appreciably from place to place, all major nosological categories seem to be present in every area for which we have adequate data. Certainly the most economical way of interpreting this finding would be that the various categories of psychoses have an organic basis, while their concrete symptomatology is largely influenced by cultural factors.

Here too, Tooth makes a striking observation in connection with the somewhat vague condition known as "delusional states." Such patients, from the less acculturated Northern Territories and from small villages with a distinctly aboriginal atmosphere in the Southern region, were, during their illness, generally taken care of by their families and only in a very few cases was restraint used —and then only within the family compound. Once the acute phase of the illness passed, the patients were encouraged to resume their normal activities and "by virtue of their peculiarities . . . acquired a certain standing in the community (*op. cit.*, p. 48). It may be said of such patients that they were treated within a familial atmosphere. By contrast, patients who had delusional states but either came from urban areas or else had been actually hospitalized, usually became quite dilapidated. Tooth suggests that if these endogenous psychotics, instead of having the good fortune of being cared for by their families, had been left to fend for themselves, they would have become the "dilapidated excentrics of the market place," while if they had been transported into an alien and restricted environment, they would have produced the symptomatology of one of the familiar varieties of schizophrenia. "In short, the form of psychosis had been determined by the treatment" (*op. cit.*, p. 48).

It is difficult to refrain from concluding that in these instances we are dealing with some basic organic—and probably physiological—disturbance, which, in the literate African, or in the African treated in a modern hospital, assumes forms which one also observes in White patients, while among the nonliterates and those treated at home, the patient exhibits a typical African set of psychiatric responses.

Since the main topic of my lectures is "culture and mental disorder" rather than "the organic etiology of psychoses," I have limited this section to a relatively brief presentation of relevant material, drawn, for the sake of cultural consistency, and consistency of diagnostic criteria used by the research worker, from one area only: The Gold Coast. However, I have little doubt that a careful perusal of the literature will strengthen the plausibility of this hypothesis, which, at the very lowest estimate, deserves a great deal of further study which, I venture to predict, will eventually bring much confirmatory material to light.

I might add that the hypothesis of an organic foundation can be appreciably strengthened also by theoretical considerations. In my first lecture I cited extensively

Devereux's views on the crucial importance of the oedipal period in the formation of that segment of the personality which may be called the "basic personality."   In the same work (*15*) he also made two other points, which I propose to utilize in a moment in connection with my hypothesis of the existence of an organic foundation for the psychoses. The first point is his insistence that psychosis invariably involves the basic personality.   Since he postulates that the basic personality is formed during the oedipal period, this aspect of his theoretical position represents a reaffirmation of the classical Freudian view of the nuclear importance of the oedipus complex in derangements of the personality and in mental disorders in general.   The second point he makes is his emphasis on the organism's self-healing potential—the *vis medicatrix naturae*—a matter which he takes up once more, elsewhere, with special reference to what most people call the "infantile neuroses" and which he, with greater specificity, calls "the developmental neuroses."*   He distinguishes between the "developmental neuroses" and the "genuine neuroses" of childhood, precisely on the basis of the fact that the former are "outgrown" exclusively through the organic impetus provided by the maturation of the organism.

It seems to me that Devereux's views regarding the role of the oedipal period in the formation of the basic personality and regarding the invariable involvement of the basic personality in the psychoses can be tied up with the specific chronology of the development of the child's nervous system.   Indeed, the child's nervous system is

---

* The reference here is to a paper by George Devereux (*16*), which Professor Linton read in manuscript, just before his death. [*Ed.*]

not complete and not fully myelinized until the third or fourth year of life, i.e., *not until the time when the oedipus complex usually comes into being.* I suspect that it is this incompleteness of the infant's nervous system which explains why Devereux insists—rightly, in my opinion— that the basic personality is simply not susceptible of coming into being until the onset of the oedipal period . . . i.e., not until the nervous system is completed. Indeed, he duly emphasises the complexities of the experi- ences—requiring the capacity to generalize, at least uncon- sciously, the concrete experiences which occur day after day to the point of sensing the pattern which is the common denominator of these experiences; and he derives the basic personality from this *generalized* experience rather than from the concrete experiences of everyday life.

Indeed, Devereux duly stresses that the oedipus complex involves the advanced capacity to view human beings not as "partial objects" but as *complete human beings.* He also emphasizes that the basic personality is shaped not so much by the concrete, day-to-day experiences of the infant, as by the child's generalized experience of the *pattern* underlying these concrete experiences . . . which, to my mind, likewise requires a certain degree of neural maturity. In fact, although Devereux certainly did not make this point explicitly, there is at least a latent impli- cation in his view that it is a certain amount of organic maturity—or, as I prefer to put it in this context, of neural maturity—which makes the oedipal experiences possible in the first place. It would be hard to account otherwise for the relatively late onset of the oedipus complex. And, so far as I know, everyone, except Melanie Klein (*33, 34*) and her followers are pretty much in agreement that the

oedipal period begins in the third or fourth year of life
at the earliest.

Now, it seems to me that Devereux's point, that the child
is not *capable* of having an oedipus complex, (which is
nuclear for the understanding of the psychodynamics of
mental diseases) until he is capable of relatively complex
experiences has an important corollary. If—due to its
immaturity and incomplete neural organization—the child
is not capable of having experiences of sufficient complexity
to develop a basic personality, then, it seems to me, it can
likewise not experience *sufficiently severe* traumata either.
This view is materially strengthened by the previously
mentioned view concerning the healing effects of the
intensity of the growth process in the child, which is never
again in life quite as strong as it is in childhood.   And, as
stated above, it is precisely this developmental push or
sweep which, according to Devereux, enables the child to
overcome, without psychiatric help, what he terms "developmental neuroses," in contradistinction to the true neuroses occurring in childhood.

By contrast the older child, with his relatively more
developed neural organization, is more aware of conse-
quences, more inclined to anxiety—and anxiety is the
crucial aspect of all mental disturbances—and more likely
to experience truly traumatic shocks. I remind you in this
context of what I said in Chapter I regarding the child's
inability to understand the complexities of the adult world
and of adult behavior. The infant is not even aware of
them, or, otherwise expressed, he only experiences the
impact of complexity, but does not sense the complexity
in itself and is therefore not bewildered by it. The bigger
child does, however, have a sufficient neural maturity both

to experience the impact of the complex world and to sense the puzzling complexity thereof *sufficiently* to be *traumatized* by it. I want to remind you in this context that it is precisely this type of "disorientation" which was considered by Devereux (*12*) to be of fundamental importance in the genesis of schizophrenia.

Of course, I suspect that some of the "healing effects" of the very intense maturational process in the small child are, in the case of the more mature and neurally normal child, taken over by the increased defensive potentialities of his more developed nervous system. If, however, a child's nervous system has some fundamental inadequacy, this child will still have the capacity of being *traumatized* and confused by the complexities of the world of adults, *but* will *not* be able to *defend* himself against this trauma as adequately as a neurally normal child can.

While some of the preceding considerations are admittedly in need of further investigation, I think they do represent the inevitable organic implications of Devereux's views regarding the functional and chronological relationship between the onset of the oedipal period and the evolving of a basic personality, as well as of his thesis that the basic personality is always involved in the psychoses.

It would be hazardous indeed in the present state of our knowledge to do more than raise the question of an organic basis in psychoses, and to suggest a framework for the exploration of this problem. Also, since the main topic of my lectures is "culture and mental disorders" and not "the organic basis of the psychoses" I have limited this section to a relatively brief consideration of the latter problem. I have drawn my clinical data from a single area—the Gold Coast—and from a single author—Tooth—

in order to insure that there would be both a cultural consistency and a diagnostic consistency in the data cited. For the same reason, in my discussion of the theoretical background of this hypothesis I have leaned toward Devereux's views, which form a consistent scheme.

In conclusion I can only say that while I have stated my views in the form of a working hypothesis, I have little doubt that a careful perusal of the literature and further field research alike will strengthen the plausibility of this hypothesis which, at the lowest estimate, seems to deserve further study.

THE INCIDENCE OF MENTAL DISORDERS

The main difficulty in studying mental disorders in primitive groups is that exceedingly little information has been obtained so far about the incidence of such disorders in the total population, as well as about the ratio between the various types of mental disorders, and about the differential incidence of mental disorders—and of sub-categories of mental disorders—in various social strata, in any society which does not have adequate facilities for the hospitalization of such patients. In addition, there are also a good many practical obstacles to a detailed investigation of such statistical problems.

One of the principal difficulties is that even an actual census of the mentally deranged in some primitive group is likely to make it appear that psychosis is rarer among primitives than among ourselves, simply because only a few harmless psychotics can survive for any length of time in a primitive society. This remark may seem startling, in view of the fact that there are many statements to the effect that "primitives" respect the psychotic. It cannot be denied that they do usually regard them with fear and considerable awe. However, I am certain that there is no society in which the genuine psychotic occupies a favored social position. As you will see from our discussion of hysteria (Chapter III), *in order to exploit the advantages of abnormal behavior one must be capable of appraising situations in realistic terms and of devising behavior which would be advantageous to one. The inability to do this is, to my mind, the real test of psychosis.* The medicine men, prophets and the like, who gain prestige and acquire wealth and power through their abnormal behavior, are hysterics or neurotics, and not true psychotics. It is precisely this fact which enables them to exploit their own abnormality for purposes of gain, and to make it, so to speak, "pay dividends." This is an ability which, to my mind, the psychotic does not possess.

Be that as it may, one thing seems certain: The idea that in primitive society the psychotic is, so to speak, "sitting on top of the world" is decidedly wrong. There are no societies I know of in which the psychotic is admired or given high social status.

I readily admit that primitive peoples very frequently treat the psychotics well. Sometimes this may be due to the belief that the psychotic is possessed by evil spirits, so that people are afraid to incur the hostility and wrath of those spirits. However, the observation that, in practice, the psychotic is *treated* well in some societies must not obscure the fundamental fact that, in the last resort, psychotics are not *liked*. The notion that the psychotic is favored in primitive society is, thus, another one of those many assumptions regarding mental disorder in primitive groups which we cannot support by actual information.

Psychotics of the catatonic variety, who can't take care of themselves, are usually just allowed to die. Now and then there will be some very devoted relative, perhaps a son, or a wife, who will try to take care of such a psychotic, but, since there are no real facilities for ministering to them, even these caretakers finally get bored, and the psychotic is allowed to "pass out." The violent psychotics, particularly those in the manic phase of the manic-depressive cycle, are as a rule just too much of a nuisance for the group. Hence, in practically all societies there are handy rationalizations for getting rid of them. For example, if the psychotic is not believed to be possessed, it is thought that at least his soul is missing. I will remark here in passing that the idea of a detachable soul is a very wide-spread one, and often provides the best rationalization of dreams, hysteric phenomena, psychoses, etc. Where such beliefs are held, the people readily come to feel that the psychotic's soul is "gone." This makes sense to them, since most primitives make a distinction between soul and life, and regard the vital functions as perfectly able to "carry on" even when the soul is away. In proof of this view they cite the occurrence of vigorous dreams, during which the dreamer may wander far afield and do all sorts of things while he is asleep, but breathing and alive; and insist that, despite these experiences of the wandering soul, the dreamer "comes to" the next morning. From this theory it is but a step to the view that the psychotic is a person whose soul has wandered off. Hence, if he stays insane for any length of time, they conclude that it is merely the vital functions of the body which are making trouble, and that his soul is "gone" for good. Therefore they "quiet him down" with a club, or strangling cord, or what have you. Then they give him a good funeral and everybody is satisfied. All this may sound very matter of fact to you, but you must understand that, in many cases, the native simply has no other alternative. Of course, you must not think that even the most harassed primitive is so callous as to knock a troublesomely psychotic kinsman over the head without any compunction. I remember being told in Madagascar that when the news spread around that the French had established mental hospitals for the natives, people from remote villages packed up their most troublesome and violently psychotic relatives and undertook arduous journeys to deliver them alive to these hospitals—delighted with being offered an alternative to having to kill them. Facts of this type explain why we simply don't know what the incidence of psychosis in primitive society really is.

Of course, occasionally one does obtain accounts of psychotic individuals or evidence concerning psychosis. Thus, many years ago, when I was in Aztec, New Mexico, I came across what I was pretty sure was evidence of the confinement of an insane person. In an old *kiva*, which is a circular, subterranean room, we found the skeleton of an adult male, about forty-five years old, who obviously had not been buried. The skeleton lay sprawled in such a way that the corpse could not have been laid in a grave. Furthermore, the floor of this *kiva* was completely covered with bowls and jars, all of which had been broken. The only thing that we could figure out was that this individual had been a psychotic, probably of a manic type, but, nevertheless, had been too important a man for the tribe to dispose of. So, apparently, they didn't kill him, but confined him in this pit, and then lowered food to him. Our supposition was that the jars we found were the containers in which the food had been given him.

One other thing to be mentioned is that a small society can be quite tolerant of queer people. Thus, any backwoods American community will have people, some of whom are feeble-minded while others may be psychotics of the harmless and non-troublesome variety, whom they do not cause to be hospitalized. The community knows them fairly well, and even though there is an occasional explosion, such as a murder, most of the time these people are fitted into the community, and are taken care of by their relatives. Even a supposedly very harsh and suspicious group, like the people of Dobu, manages occasionally to be very lenient toward the more troublesome mentally deranged persons belonging to their village. Fortune (*21*) gives us a good account of such an attitude in Dobu.

He states that public opinion is lenient toward the insane and the delinquent, although he mentions the possibility that this kindly treatment may be due to the absence of a proper social machinery for dealing with them. He cites three specific instances. The first case is that of a man who was mildly insane and showed two principal forms of deranged behavior, both of which elicited a far from unkind social reaction. His first abnormality consisted in his touching, in a playfully amorous manner, women whom no Dobuan in his right senses would have flirted with publicly. Yet, even the women whom he touched were kind to him, tried to humor him and sought to divert his attention to other matters. His second abnormality was a wholly inordinate and compulsive love of work for its own sake, so that he would do anything for anyone who asked him to work for him.   In addition, when such work was unavailable, he worked strenuously and incessantly on his own.   Yet, although here was a person practically asking to be exploited and taken advantage of, people felt that he was basically a good fellow, who had hard enough a life due to his compulsion to exert himself, and therefore little advantage was taken of his readiness to work for anyone without remuneration.   The second case is that of an *amok* runner.   The Dobuans even sought to restrain a man running *amok* in a manner which would not injure him, and the next day, after the man recovered from his seizure, they refrained from saying anything which would have made him uncomfortable by reminding him of something he did the night before, and which had since been blanketed by amnesia.   The third case is that of a woman, called Negwadi, who stole everything she could. No magic could control her and people cursed her continually, though not to her face, since that would not have accomplished anything.   Hence, the Dobuans, one of whose main themes in life is the idea of controlling everything by magic, assumed what can only be called a humorous attitude toward this delinquent person, whom nothing could control (*21*, pp. 53–56).

I am sure I don't have to labor the point that attempts of this type to overlook the mentally ill person's derelictions and to manage him in the home environment do not help us greatly to obtain a clearcut picture of the incidence of mental disorders in societies which have no facilities for the hospitalization of the psychotic.   Please note that I say "psychotic" quite specifically.   The situation is even more complicated in the case of the neurotic, who—especially if he is a hysteric—can often get along in society; he may even attain a position of importance, and is, thus, not thought of as a "mental case." Somewhat anticipating my further discussion, I want to mention that, according to Stainbrook (57), in Bahia, Brazil, the hysteric, who can manage his hysteria in conventional ways, can join the *Candomble* ritual group, whereas the frank psychotic and especially schizophrenic would be "screened out" during the probationary period, as too idiosyncratic in the manifestations of his psychopathology.

The best statistical data we have seen to come from Africa . . . though even there Carothers (6) opens his discussion of the incidence of mental disorders with the terse statement "Figures can lie" and, a few lines further, speaks of a "jungle of statistics."

As regards *total incidence* Carothers states that "certified lunatics" in England and Wales in 1938 were four per 1000 population, while at roughly the same time there were in the Gold Coast 0.3 per 1000, in Nyasaland 0.06 per 1000, in Kenya Colony 0.1 per 1000, and in South Africa 1.2 per 1000. New admissions in England and Wales were fifty-seven per 100,000 population, the corresponding figures for Kenya Colony being 3.4, for the Gold Coast 3.3, and for South Africa 15.4. In French Togoland there seem to be roughly four insane per 1000 population.

As regards *sex incidence*, the rate of male and female insane is about the same as the rate given for Occidental countries by Henderson and Gillespie (26). By contrast, in Africa hospitalized male psychotics greatly predominate over females, especially in backward areas. The ratios vary from about 6:1 at Zomba, at Accra and in Nigeria, to 1.5:1 in reports given by Gold Coast chiefs to

Tooth, concerning psychotics in rural areas. This great range is partly due to a higher ratio of admissions from the male groups working in labor camps, army barracks and townships, which explains the high ratio (6:1) for, e.g., Accra. Yet males seem to predominate even under aboriginal conditions in the rural villages (1.5:1 mentioned above). This latter ratio may, however, be as low as it is only because native women lead relatively sheltered lives.

As regards *age incidence* Carothers notes that 78% of all institutionalized African psychotics are admitted between the ages of ten to forty, while in the U.S.A., in Dayton, only 42% of new admissions belong to this age span. While there are undoubtedly many sources of error here, Carothers nonetheless feels that the young adult group constitutes a larger proportion of first admissions in Africa than it does in the U.S.A., even after being corrected.

The degree of *detribalization,* or loss of contact with one's cultural heritage and milieu, does, according to Carothers, affect the incidence of psychosis. He cites for Kenya Colony the following ratios: For tribal natives 2.3 per 100,000, for squatters on land owned by Whites 2.5, and for Africans living away from the home environment 13.3. He contrasts this with Tooth's admittedly indirect proof that Westernization does not increase the incidence of psychosis, and therefore is critical of Tooth's views. While I admit that Tooth's series is fairly small and his reasoning complex and partly indirect, I feel that this is a point where Tooth's views deserve further study, for reasons which I hinted at in connection with my discussion of the organic substratum in psychoses.

In the same work Carothers also discusses the differential incidence of the various mental disorders observed in Africans, both by himself and by others. I will comment only in passing on the fact that practically all categories of mental disorders known to us through the study of Occidental patients are also observed in Africa, though often with somewhat different symptomatologies and that they frequently constitute a different percentage of the total hospitalized population than is the case in England or the United States.

It would be extremely time consuming to go into great detail on this point, particularly since—as many psychiatrists have stressed—diagnoses change even in our mental hospitals, and often reflect the theoretical orientation of the diagnostician. I might add that psychiatrically sophisticated anthropologists are also of this opinion. Thus, Devereux tells me that Laubscher (38) has been criticized for his overly great proneness to diagnose schizophrenia in South Africans, and added that, after seeing a film of African patients taken by Laubscher, he himself was strongly inclined to concur with this criticism. On the other hand, Carothers criticizes Tooth for using the nosological category "delusional states" and suggests that these cases should be properly designated as "schizophrenias" of an amorphous type. I certainly feel unqualified to settle such disagreements between psychiatric experts in diagnosis, though—since I made appreciable use of Tooth's views in my discussion of the organic substratum of the psychoses—I would like to add that in this instance there is much to be said in favor of Tooth. For example, I recall Devereux telling me repeatedly how necessary it is to revive the now more or less obsolete term "transitory delusional states" for the proper description of mental disorders in primitive society.

In view of this confused situation, I will simply try to highlight some of the main points cited by Carothers in regard to the differential incidence of various mental disorders in Africa, and will then devote most of my attention to the problem of schizophrenia.

One fact stressed by Carothers is that neither he nor Tooth had ever seen a *mongolic defective* in Africa, and adds that this is probably not due to the fact that few mongolics could survive under aboriginal conditions, since, before becoming a psychiatrist, Carothers himself was a general medical officer, who would have seen mongolics had there been any among African children. Carothers mentions this fact, but declares himself unable to explain it.

Carothers also shows that *paranoia, paraphrenia and even paranoid schizophrenia* are rare among Africans. He bases his statement primarily on data from British possessions in Africa, but also cites Aubin's (1) comment regarding Negroes from French Africa, to the effect that the relatively most advanced subjects have the most accentuated paranoid tendencies, in which persecutory delusions are the rule, while megalomania is relatively exceptional. This leads Carothers to suggest that the latter requires a higher degree of systematization. He also cites Aubin to the effect that the supernatural component is evident in many delusions of persecution, and Tooth regarding the fact that only the literate African feels persecuted by electricity and the wireless. These findings tally closely with Stainbrook's (57) data concerning Negroes of Bahia, Brazil, which I propose to discuss in paragraphs which appear later.

Turing now to *affective disorders,* Carothers doubts that the differentiation between manic and depressive psychosis is as useful in Africa as it is when one deals with White patients. He states that both are far from being frequent in Africans, and discusses in detail the fact that manics greatly outnumber depressives. Thus, of thirty-four patients considered to be suffering from abnormal "affective states," Tooth diagnosed only six as depressives. Carothers likewise saw only twenty-four depressives among 1,508 patients admitted to a mental hospital over a period of ten years, while Laubscher is cited to the effect that of 1,700 cases admitted over a period of fifteen years only seven had tried to kill themselves either before or during hospitalization. Laubscher also stated that self mutilation too is very rare.

In explanation of this rarity of depression in African psychotics Carothers suggests that depression requires a rather high degree of personality integration, and a sense of the continuity of the person, involving a sense of retribution and of personal responsibility . . . and adds that Tooth found self reproach very rare indeed in African psychotics. Here, again, Stainbrook's Bahian Negro data converge so closely with those we have from Africa, that his findings deserve to be examined in some detail.

The most interesting and most readily comparable results from outside Africa seem to me to be those reported from Bahia in Northern Brazil, by Stainbrook (57). These data are of particular interest, since they too refer to subjects who were predominantly Negro, and who, furthermore, preserve to this day at least some of the cults and cult organizations of their African forebears. In addition, the fact that Bahia had been subjected to a sound sociological investigation, which included the definition of three ecological areas, enabled Stainbrook to relate his findings to clearcut, empirically ascertained, social and cultural patterns, which facilitated the study of the possible cultural determinants of the psychopathology found in that area.

Most of the patients studied by Stainbrook were hospitalized in the psychiatric hospital at Salvador, capital of the state of Bahia. About 80% of them came from rural areas, and a good many from the three definitely established ecological areas. Eighty-five per cent belonged to the lower class, and the other 15% to the middle class. Most of them were Negroes or of mixed blood, many of them were illiterate and the majority exhibited behavior patterns demonstrating both African and Brazilian influences. Probably due to the social and also the hospital class structure, the patients were inclined to be passive and obedient, and to exhibit little aggressivity. On the whole, women were more aggressive than men, but even they usually retained their habits of modesty as regards the concealment of their legs while squatting in their traditional posture. The greater inclination of women to express affect may explain why Bahian psychiatrists diagnosed four times as many women as men as being in the manic phase of a manic depressive psychosis. It should also be stressed that in the lower class patients depressive reactions are extremely rare . . . to the point that no lower class patient committed suicide in the hospital during the last ten years. This tallies closely with African data.

As regards schizophrenics, a strikingly large number of them had lost their parents before entering the hospital. It is not easy to decide whether this is significant since, in Bahian society, the mother's kin would provide substitute mothering, to replace the home disrupted by death. On the other hand, the hospital records indicate for these patients a life-long deficiency in object relationships and a consistent withdrawal pattern.   However, the withdrawal was seldom so pronounced as to lead to stupor and it was usually not difficult to elicit a meaningful response even from schizophrenics.   Even catatonics were not beyond reach.   "One catatonic girl . . . spoke to me in spite of the fact that she was retaining food in her mouth and had widely dilated 'catatonic' pupils and other gross neurophysiological indices of extreme fear and an almost complete motor inhibition" (*op. cit.*, pp. 332–3).   This girl, after voicing her fear of spirits added that she was not afraid of people "because they were human beings" (*op. cit.*, p. 333).

Fear and anxiety in lower class patients were chiefly rooted in ideas of retribution related both to Catholic and African religion, and restitution symptoms, such as megalomania and delusions of persecution, were formulated in religious terms.   Middle-class men, by contrast, developed more secular restitutional symptoms, related to wealth and class, and their persecutory ideas were more frequently related to other human beings.   This fact seems to be related to the social mobility aspirations of the Bahian middle class, while the lower classes have no self conscious class aspirations.   Also, upward social mobility usually involves, for men at least, a decrease in religious involvements.   As regards impersonal "persecutors" such as electricity, they were rare even in middle class people, and were found only in patients hospitalized in a private sanatorium.   These findings, too, dovetail with our African data.

A close relationship seems to exist between individual psychopathology and the ritual possession connected with the *Candomble* ritual, which is of African origin. Thus, it has been noted that only 3–5% of the female psychiatric population had been actual members of that cult. However, Stainbrook rightly stresses that while this cult certainly affords its members important gratifications "such an individual must be in sufficient control of autistic and regressive behavior and of reality-testing to be acceptable within the relatively rigid ritualistic group action. Hence, no frankly schizophrenic person would be able to pass the probationary scrutiny (*op. cit.*, p. 334). Hysterics who used hysterical dissociation in a frankly idiosyncratic way were also excluded. This means that admission to *Candomble* membership involved something not unlike a superficial psychiatric screening. In this connection Stainbrook also notes that gross hysterical manifestations are not common among Bahian Negroes: Some women who belonged to the *Candomble* and were unable to experience the ritually induced dissociation, usually showed exceptional amounts of anxiety and also stubbornness and hostility.

On the other hand female schizophrenics of the lower class frequently enacted a *Candomble* type of possession by some African god, or goddess. Yet, even in these cases the clinical picture was clearly not hysterical but schizophrenic and usually represented a reaction to some situational stress or deprivation. It involved a temporary *introjection* of the deity, which corresponds to the ritual *identification* with the deity in *Candomble* "possession" phenomena. Stainbrook also notes that whereas the *Yoruba Candomble* group does not seem to allow the institutionalization of psychotic behavior, the *Caboclo* and *Macumba* derivatives of this cult had many psychiatrically abnormal members.

Finally, Stainbrook notes an interesting fact regarding *social* differentiation between normal and abnormal in Bahian society. He states that whereas hallucinatory experiences do not cause a person's fellows to view him as abnormal, aggressive behavior stamps him as *"malucco"* and leads to his hospitalization.

What we have to retain from these findings is chiefly the demonstration that a given disease entity, such as schizophrenia, which, in our society, may result in a distinctive clinical picture, can, in another society, show marked deviations from our textbook picture of schizophrenic behavior. To my mind, the most noteworthy example of this fact to be found in the Bahian material is the relative accessibility to human relationships of even withdrawn and catatonic patients.

A really satisfactory explanation of these differences is not available at present. In regard to the last point I made, I would suggest that the membership of the individual in a closely knit kin group of considerable size, from which he derives much security and emotional satisfactions, may militate against the development of withdrawal in psychotic states. Certainly Tooth's already mentioned remarks on the different pictures presented by patients suffering from delusional states who were kept at home, by those who strayed into urban environments and by those who were hospitalized, seem to support this interpretation. I am also inclined to attach considerable importance to the possibility that a culture which permits violent emotional expressions and lays little emphasis on logical thinking, may—because of these features—prevent the development of self-reproach reactions. These are tentative working hypotheses, whose chief purpose is to underscore that much more work of this type will have to be done before a definite answer may be given to questions of this nature.

And, since I am just now discussing working hypotheses, I might as well add that even racial factors cannot be wholly ruled out a priori in this context . . . at least not until we have comparable samples from non-Negro groups.

PSYCHOSIS AND SOCIAL CLASS

There is practically no information on the incidence of psychoses in different social classes in non-European societies. Even in our own society we have very little information on this point. In the words of Hollingshead and Redlich (29): "Neither psychiatrists nor sociologists have carried on extensive research into the . . . interrelations between the class structure and the development of mental illness. However, a few sociologists and psychiatrists have written speculative and research papers in this area (*op. cit.*, p. 163). Some work along this line has been attempted in our own society, the most significant and most recent being that, now under way, by Hollingshead, Redlich and associates in New Haven. This city was chosen because it had already been subjected to intensive social investigations, making the placement of individuals in terms of class unusually easy. The data collected so far already show an extraordinary difference in the frequency of schizophrenia in the various classes, the incidence—expressed in percentages—in the lowest class being twelve and one-half times as high as in the highest class, with the intervening classes intermediate in this respect. For the five social classes into which the population was divided by this research group, the following indices of prevalence of schizophrenia were found:

I	22
II	33
III	43
IV	88
V	246 (*op. cit.*, p. 168)

The same authors also found that the incidence of the total psychiatric population, i.e., of psychiatric patients of all types—gradually increases as one descends in the social scale:

Class	% of Normal Population	% of Psychiatric Population
I	3.1	1.0
II	8.1	6.7
III	22.0	13.2
IV	46.0	38.6
V	17.8	36.8
Unknown	3.0	3.7 (*op. cit.*, p. 167)

It seems certain that numerous factors other than social and economic stress influence this picture, and further study is therefore needed.

The situation regarding the incidence of neurosis in various social classes is also an interesting one in New Haven. Hollingshead and Redlich found that whereas the incidence of psychoses increases as we descend in the social scale, the incidence of neuroses diminishes. This is supported by the following data concerning the psychiatric populations of various classes:

Social Class	% of Neuroses	% of Psychoses
I	52.6	47.4
II	67.2	32.8
III	44.2	55.8
IV	23.1	76.9
V	8.4	91.6 (*op. cit.*, p. 167)

This inverse ratio of the incidence of neuroses and psychoses in various classes is quite striking and the authors themselves feel that, so far, they have not been able to find a satisfactory explanation of this finding.

THE PROBLEM OF THE NEUROSES

Neuroses are much more difficult to define than psychoses and confront non-psychiatrists, from whom most of our information about "primitive" societies is derived, with greater difficulties of detection and description. What informal observations we have, support the view that neuroses are present in all societies, although, unfortunately, here we have—if possible—even fewer clues as to their relative frequency than we have in the case of psychoses. What observations we do possess clearly suggest that the behavior of neurotics is much more thoroughly culturally conditioned than is the behavior of psychotics. This thesis is certainly true of hysteria, as will be seen from our description and analysis of that neurosis in Chapter III.

The situation, as regards collecting data on neuroses by anthropologists, is further complicated by the fact that certain forms of neurotic behavior receive definite cultural encouragement. Sometimes this encouragement is so strong that we may legitimately speak of a cultural conditioning of neurotic behavior. The classical case is probably that of the shaman or medicine man, whose hysterical proclivities certainly do receive a great deal of social support and earn him definite psychological and also tangible rewards. This point will be discussed in some detail in Chapter III, and need not arrest our attention any further at this juncture. I am also quite certain that my statement that magical rituals would be particularly congenial to obsessive neurotics will not startle anyone familiar with Freud's work on the nexus between ritual and obsession (22), and that it would therefore be supererogatory for me to labor this point and to document it with examples of complex magical rites which, in order to be deemed effective, have to be executed with great and meticulous accuracy. Instead, I will turn to other aspects of the problems of neurosis in other societies, which are of more general import to psychiatric theory.

The universal presence of neuroses raises interesting theoretical questions regarding their genesis. It does not bear out at least the layman's oversimplified version of Freud's theory that they always originate in sexual repression, naively defined by the laymen as sexual deprivation resulting from generalized social pressures against cohabitation and from the guilt resulting when tabooed coital behavior did take place. Indeed, neuroses are known to occur even in societies in which the free expression of the sexual drive is limited only by a few object taboos, defined in terms of the incest barrier. It seems more probable to me that neurosis may result from the frustration of *any primary drive*. Thus, I feel that—in cooperation with Kardiner—it is possible to state with a fair degree of accuracy that in the Marquesas neurotic expressions center about food rather than about sexual *deprivation,* of which there is little indeed in those islands.*

The much disputed problem of the *oedipus complex* is also illuminated by cross-cultural studies. It seems safe to say that this complex, or its equivalent, is present in all societies. The difficulties which seem to arise in locating the oedipus complex everywhere appear to be due to the use of a too narrow—and too narrowly "sexual"—definition of this complex. It has been occasionally stated that in some societies the oedipus complex is absent. Thus, Malinowski (46) was of the opinion that it did not exist in the Trobriand Islands, where—due to the native belief that the father has no share in procreating the child and is therefore not related to him—the father is not the person in authority over the child. It is my opinion, shared by a good many of my psychoanalytically sophisticated anthropological colleagues, that in such situations the oedipal attitudes are not directed at the *real* father, but at the mother's brother, who—being, in a matrilineal system of descent, the child's closest male relative—*assumes the disciplinary and rewarding functions which, among ourselves, are associated with biological fatherhood.* The most probable interpretation to be offered here is that oedipal hostilities are not determined primarily by the child's sexual jealousy of the father, but by his more generalized resentment of anyone who interferes with his mother's attentions to him, to which is added his ambivalent attitude toward the frustrating-rewarding male, regardless of who this male may be, and how he happens to be related to the child. I think that

---

* This view would hold regardless of whether or not one agrees with Freud in considering eating a partially libidinal i.e., in the broad sense "sexual" pleasure, or views eating simply as a basic physiological need involving also certain corresponding psychological drives. [*Ed.*]

this formulation would be acceptable even to the majority of thoughtful psychoanalysts, since all that this view implies is a minimization of the importance of the specific father-child biological and kinship tie, and the stressing of the importance of the *actual role* which a related male— be he father, maternal uncle or what not—plays in the life of the child.

In conclusion, it seems to me that cross-cultural studies will be particularly rewarding in this field. In the first place, even the limited data available at present suggest that, in neurosis as in psychosis, there may be an under-lying constitutional factor, since in all societies many individuals undergo experiences which make only *some* people neurotic, but leave the majority, who also had such experiences, non-neurotic. On the other hand, both in psychoses and in neuroses the *precipitating stresses* may be closely related to the stability or instability of culture. Adequately learned responses are important conservers of energy and reducers of stress, while the making of decisions is a definite strain. However, since the continued effectiveness of adequately learned responses is contingent on cultural stability, we may say with a reasonable degree of assurance that the current psychiatric situation in the United States is a function of the rapid change currently characteristic of our society.

III

Hysteria in Cultural Perspective

HOMOSEXUALITY

The present chapter will be devoted primarily to hysteria. However, in order to clarify the influence of social and cultural factors upon the actual manifestations of a mental disorder, and in order to elucidate the nature of the gratifications which the emotionally disturbed person may derive from his abnormal condition, I propose to lead up to the main topic by discussing, at least briefly, homosexuality in a cultural perspective. This discussion will simplify our attempt to understand the cultural aspects of hysteria. Indeed, homosexuality cannot be considered a psychological aberration fully comparable to neuroses and psychoses, since it is institutionalized in many societies.

We must make an initial distinction between real homosexuality—i.e., behavior focussed on sexual relations with persons of the same sex—and the adoption of the opposite sex role, in which playing the social and cultural role of the opposite sex seems to be the decisive factor. This "role playing" often involves also transvestitism, or "cross dressing," i.e., the wearing of the garb of the opposite sex.

It is quite striking that the adoption of the female social role by males is much more common than is the adoption of the male role by females. This may be due to two factors:

(1) Prestige differences between male and female status.

(2) Functional disabilities of women.

Prestige differences. On the whole, in most societies men occupy a higher prestige position than do the women. Now, it stands to reason that higher prestige positions are everywhere more protected against invasion than are lower prestige positions. Hence, it is always harder to rise in society than it is to descend to a lower estate. This is one reason for assuming that differences in prestige between men and women may account for the fact that whereas men are relatively free to assume female social roles, females find it rather difficult to lay claim to the masculine role simply by dressing up as men.

Functional disabilities. On the whole, it is easier for men to perform feminine functions, than for women to perform masculine ones. Thus, in our own society, cooking and sewing are chiefly feminine functions. Nonetheless, the world's most famous cooks and dressmakers are almost invariably men. The same is true of really famous hairdressers, interior decorators and teachers. As regards this latter group, women predominate at the elementary school level, while men predominate at the college level. By contrast, women find it more difficult to perform some typically masculine activities, sometimes through lack of strength and at other times through lack of pugnaciousness. For example the world has known some renowned woman warriors, but their fame is based more upon the fact that they were women than upon the true greatness of their military exploits, which pale in comparison with those of great male generals and fighters. The Countess of Forli or the Rajput Queen who defended their castles with great tenacity are certainly not comparable to Napoleon as generals, or to Bayard as fighters.

Even where female fighting units exist, as among the Fon in Africa—and the female Fon regiments were supposed to be good fighters—we are dealing with a highly localized and exceptional situation.

Likewise, a good many characteristically masculine pursuits demand a degree of physical strength of which the average woman simply is not capable . . . especially where sudden violent exertion is involved. Thus, while women are the porters in many areas, it is hard to visualize most women as lumberjacks.

Of course, there are some known instances of females assuming the male role. Among the Blackfoot we have the so-called "manly-hearted woman" described for us in detail by Oscar Lewis (39). These women were domineering and ran their own enterprises but were not—characteristically or necessarily—either transvestites or homosexuals. The combined transvestite-homosexual role of women in Mohave society was described by Devereux (11), but he made it clear that the initiation of women into male status was very informal in comparison to the formal initiation of males into female status, and that the female transvestite had, on the whole, a harder time than did the male transvestite. Also, Devereux mentions several male transvestites and only one female one.

By contrast, the assumption of the female role by males is much more common.

In Madagascar (40) we have transvestites, called *sarombavy*, which seem to exist in all Malagasy tribes. The Tanala say that such men exhibit feminine traits from birth. They dress like women, arrange their hair like women and pursue feminine occupations such as weaving. There was no rule against their becoming medicine men or against their showing supernatural powers, but my informants never heard of such powers being shown by a *sarombavy*. The attitude toward them was, on the whole, neutral.

The Bara (Madagascar) *sarombavy* included hermaphrodites, homosexuals and impotent men. The hermaphrodites dressed like women from birth, while the others did so at puberty or later. Many professional Bara dancers are homosexuals, and some of these become *sarombavy* or else fluctuate between male and female roles. Thus, one dancer became a transvestite for a while, but eventually resumed the male dress, because he could not dance while pretending to be a woman. In one case a man who had a wife and children also married a *sarombavy,* and made him his subsidiary wife.

The case of those *sarombavy* who assumed this role due to impotency is psychologically of great interest. Since women discuss the virility of their lovers rather freely, if a man is impotent or feeble, this fact will become widely known and the women will jeer at him. Hence, some men, who have doubts regarding their own virility, sometimes become *sarombavy* at puberty. I know of two such men, who lived as women but showed no homosexual inclinations. The most interesting case that came to my notice was that of a sixty year old Betsileo widower with grown children, who lived among the Bara. At the age of fifty-two or fifty-three a severe illness left him both impotent and unable to do heavy work. He therefore became a *sarombavy,* learned to weave and earned his living by selling the cloth he had woven. This commanded considerable respect. I have been unable to discover any indication that Tanala or other Malagasy women ever became transvestites and adopted the male role.

What seems to me of crucial importance in understanding the phenomenon of *sarombavy* among the Tanala is the fact that no head of a household and no oldest son has been known to become a *sarombavy.** Transvestites seem to be recruited exclusively from the ranks of younger sons, who are wholly subordinated to their father and oldest brother. Apparently transvestitism is one of the "outs" available to these younger sons whose status in the family and in society is not one affording appreciable ego gratification (30).

In aboriginal America the male transvestite pattern was fairly widespread and is commonly designated by anthropologists by the term "berdache." In a good many Indian societies the berdache was not without prestige. Some Plains Indians held that they excelled in female work, and that their porcupine quill embroidery was above average in quality. In some Southwestern tribes such as the Pima (28) boys showing potential female inclinations were subjected to a test, by being forced to choose between a typically masculine object and a typically feminine one. If they chose the female object, they were offically considered transvestites. Among the Plains Indians, transvestitism was often the result of a vision. In that area young men deliberately sought a vision, in order to gain power in life, and this vision set a pattern for their subsequent career. Among the Omaha Indians the vision sometimes encouraged the youth to become a berdache,

---

* The previously mentioned widower with grown children was a Betsileo, not a Tanala. [*Ed.*]

the supernatural authority which sanctioned this being usually the moon.

Berdaches seldom married, though we do have isolated records of such marriages, for example among the Mohave (*11*). However, even among the Mohave such marriages were rather unstable and stormy ones, being often little more than interludes between two heterosexual marriages of the non-transvestite spouse. This instability was apparently largely due to the fact that, despite the institutionalization of transvestitism among the Mohave, the non-transvestite spouse in such couples was pretty consistently ridiculed and teased.

An entirely different matter is culturally incorporated homosexuality. This is usually not associated with the reversal of social sex roles. In Madagascar dancers were often homosexual. In some other instances this type of homosexuality was associated with a lack of access to women—typically among the unmarried.

In still other groups bisexuality is simply taken for granted. The best known example of this is classical Greece, where adolescent boys often had socially highly valued and also quite intensively romanticized relations with adult men, but, in due course—after outgrowing the adolescent stage—switched to a predominantly male sexual pattern, marrying, begetting children and the like. Bisexuality is also known to exist and to be taken for granted among the Arabs and in many parts of Melanesia.

THE HYSTERIAS

The second topic to be discussed in this lecture concerns the interrelations of culture and hysteria. Unfortunately, hysteria is exceedingly difficult to define. At least, I

have not come across any definition which seemed to me
to be perfectly adequate. Hysteria is one of those things
on which we have a general consensus of opinion as to
what it is—an agreement that certain states are hysteric—
but it is very hard to find a definition which is sufficiently
extensive to be satisfactory and yet is not applicable also
to other phenomena. I would suggest that perhaps the
best working definition is that in hysteric states the conscious mind temporarily releases its control to the sub-
conscious.*

Hysteria certainly differs from psychosis at the behavioral level, in that the hysteric retains a sense of reality
even in the course of seizure. In other words, the hysteric
always responds to a greater or less degree to external
cues. For instance, even though he may display violent
"catatonic" behavior, go rigid, fall, and have convulsions,
etc., it is observed that the hysteric never hurts himself
unless something intervenes which he did not expect when
he began to "throw the fit." In this he differs sharply
from the real epileptic, or from certain types of psychotics.

The problem is, once more: what constitutes psychosis?
The least I can say is that all cultures recognize the differences between hysterias and psychoses. In most cases
the psychotic, the really "insane" individual, cannot be
socially integrated. He is too unreliable to be of any
use to society. Of course, certain types of psychotics have
been used as oracles, the future being foretold from their
talk or behavior, but this is most unusual.

Let us now return to the point that all societies recognize
the difference between hysterias and true psychoses. Now,
hysterias do assume a good many different forms in differ-

* Apparently the upper layers of the unconscious are meant. [*Ed.*]

ent societies and are unquestionably culturally shaped in their manifestations. The hysteric, after all, soon gives up any patterns of behavior which are not rewarding. When a person has hysteric tendencies, he learns quite a bit from observing the behavior of other hysterics and the way they are treated. This helps that person to "channel" his own hysteric manifestations. Indeed, the purpose of the various types of hysterias seems to be primarily to obtain ego satisfaction, be it only by attracting attention. Theory apart, we know for a fact that the patterns of hysteric seizures differ from one society to another; and that they can differ in the same society over a period of time. To take a very simple example from our own society, those who read Charcot's studies in hysteria, for instance, know that his *"grande hystérie,"* with its very violent physical manifestations, simply does not exist in Europe at the present time. It has "gone out of fashion." As a matter of fact, what Charcot apparently did, even in his age and time, was to take hysterics who had certain tendencies and "build them up" in the laboratory into true cases of *"grande hystérie."* Then, when they grew sufficiently violent and had sufficiently extreme physical reactions, they were rewarded for it by being pointed out as "this wonderful case," were shown to all the students, etc.

Coming a good deal closer to home, one form of hysteria which has definitely vanished within my own lifetime is that of the fainting lady. I don't know whether any of the ladies today would be able to faint on (social) demand or not. In its time fainting was certainly a very handy mechanism, because it either very seriously embarrassed any gentleman who was present or, if it did not, at least provided the lady with a perfect alibi; obviously she could have no memory of anything that had happened to her while she was unconscious. Nowadays fainting has simply "gone out." I want to stress, however, that there is no question that these Victorian faints were genuine. In my childhood I myself saw a number of them. The ladies really passed out cold, and were "brought back" usually by the process of pouring water over them, which brought them out of it very rapidly. Another technique which brought almost complete and immediate recovery was to lift up the subjects and start to stand them on their heads. This method was said to be effective because it caused the blood to flow to the brain; but whatever the reason, the fainting ladies always "snapped out of it" with great speed at this point. Here then, is an hysterical manifestation, with perfectly genuine physiological symptoms, which has disappeared from our culture. It would be exceedingly interesting to learn: (a) *how* it dropped out, and (b) how it was *learned* in the first place. It certainly was the "great stunt" of the ladies of the Victorian period.

Going somewhat further back, we come in our own society to the violent hysterical manifestations which went with the witch-trial procedures. The outbreak of witch-hunting in Salem, in particular, provides a very interesting example of cultural conditioning of hysterical responses.

It all started in the home of the Reverend Samuel Parrish, in the winter of 1692. The children of the household, Betty Parrish and her cousin Abigail Williams, were left almost entirely in the care of the Carib cook, Tituba, while Mrs. Parrish went about her good works as wife of the minister. Tituba was a slave fresh from the Barbadoes. Just what went on in the kitchen that winter no one will ever know; probably fortune-telling, séances and the telling of *voodoo* tales from Tituba's native land— plenty to excite the imagination of the Parrish children and their friends who began to gather there also to share in the entertainment.

Little girls of that period were seriously repressed. They were dressed in long confining garments such as their mothers wore; their chief forms of recreation were working samplers and playing decorously with a doll; they seldom went out in the winter except to go to church where they sat for long hours on a hard bench, listening to sermons about the wiles of the Devil and the horrors of Hell. Abigail Williams was apparently the kind of child who, in modern times, would have been tearing around on roller skates and shinnying up trees with the neighborhood boys. However, the culture of old New England provided no outlet for her energy and imagination, until Tituba's tales gave her an idea. Her first exhibition of bewitchment took place in the Parrish parlor; she began to run around on all fours and bark like a dog. This is just the sort of behavior which may occur to any eleven year old child who wants to put on an act. There is little doubt that, in the beginning, Abigail was simply playacting and not suffering from genuine hysteria. She also tried on several occasions to throw herself into the fire—but only when there were adults about to restrain her successfully.

The news of this extraordinary behavior spread like wildfire through the village and caused so much excitement and concern that soon the other young girls who had gathered in Tituba's kitchen also began to exhibit strange symptoms. Now, the adults in this society were also pretty bored and frustrated during the long cold winters, with no entertainment and little activity. The girls' dramatic behavior was therefore a phenomenon which provided a fascinating outlet also for the adults. It is interesting that, as the manifestations of witchcraft spread, the symptoms became those which are culturally associated with demonic possession, and became quite different from those which had first occurred to the inflamed imagination of an eleven year old. The victims went into convulsions and seizures, fell down insensible, foamed at the mouth, and shrieked in agony if the name of the Devil or of the person supposedly bewitching them was mentioned in their presence. This, of course, was standard behavior also for witches in Europe at the time. The victims were by this time suffering from genuine hysteria, but were definitely not psychotic. Between seizures they behaved normally; in fact, they usually came out of their "sessions" feeling refreshed and with a good appetite. The victims were almost entirely young girls, although two or three boys did get into the act also. All these youngsters were about the age of the bobby-soxers, who today scream and swoon over songs of their favorite crooner. Of course, we recognize adolescent hysteria nowadays for what it is, and therefore no one considered accusing Frank Sinatra of being a warlock. By contrast, the hysteria of these Salem teenagers was taken with a seriousness that cost the lives of many innocent people.

Now, in contrast to this earlier sort of hysteria of our not very remote ancestors, our present culture puts a premium on psychosomatic responses, and particularly on psychosomatic disorders of a rather vague and generalized nature. At the same time, typical conversion hysterias, involving a general continuing paralysis, blindness, and so forth, are not at all common in our society at the present time, and, interestingly enough, I am told that they seem to be much more frequent in the lower social categories, among uneducated peoples. Kardiner in his study of war neuroses (*31*) pointed out that this type of hysteria, psychosomatic conversion, was almost entirely limited to enlisted men. It rarely occurred in officers, the point being that, by this time, the officers know a little too much about psychology for the conscientious man—and even for the unconscious of the conscientious man—to indulge in such symptoms. Needless to say, I'm using the term "conscious" here in two quite different meanings. I mean that one can't fool such a man's conscious nowadays by the sort of block which results in paralysis, blindness, deafness or anything of that kind.

I suppose that the psychosomatic disorders of primitives should be classified under the heading of hysterias, but, unfortunately, we do not know anything about the incidence of such disorders in non-European groups. After all, it is already hard enough for the visiting anthropologist to define psychosis—and when even our doctors are unable in many cases to know whether they are dealing with psychosomatic symptoms or with hysteric symptoms, of with actual physiological derangements, one can't expect the innocent anthropological field worker to be able to diagnose such an obscure condition.

I do not doubt that disorders of this kind do occur in all societies. It is interesting to note, for example, that, among American Indians, there is a very high prevalence of gastro-intestinal disorders, which in many cases are certainly psychosomatic, because such symptoms are readily developed by a man in a state of tension or worry. Most Indians of my acquaintance did suffer from this sort of thing at one time or another, and were frequently able to name the magical cause which brought on the attack. Also, they can be cured effectively and "miraculously" by the medicine man, who, in this respect, is much superior to the white doctor. The latter will, at most, feed you bicarbonate of soda, whereas the medicine man does, after all, come with a big equipment. For example, if he is a Comanche, he comes with a basket full of rattles and fans to be used for different purposes, which are somewhat like the contents of the old-fashioned doctors' black bag. He sings four songs over his patient and uses his fan and rattle; and if they don't work, and the sick person doesn't feel better, he takes another rattle and sings four other songs. He will do this until he hits upon the particular combination which will cure the indigestion, and cure it *promptly*.

One type of presumably psychosomatic condition deserves special mention in this context. I refer here to so-called "magical death"—or *voodoo* death or death from psychic causes (5)—which seems to be some kind of extreme form of psychosomatic seizure. Here, once again, it is difficult to find out just what the incidence of such deaths really is. Even the average reservation physician can give you no information on this point, because, after all, it has only recently occurred to physicians that there are such things as psychosomatic disorders, and, as a result, they have had little time as yet to inquire into the extent to which they proliferate. I might say in passing that psychosomatic disorders seem to be the greatest source of miracles, since they can be cured by miraculous means—and often very effectively too.

Turning now to the hysterias proper, the real hysterias, I would say that they assume various forms, whose distributions can, interestingly enough, be plotted on a map. I tried once to classify these, but at that time I couldn't find any classification of hysterias in psychiatric literature which seemed to jibe at all with cultural considerations.

In the first place, the hysterias break down into those—and I'm using now a social and cultural approach—which are supposed to represent what we would call "supernatural involvement" and those which are *not* supposed to have spirits working in connection with them. In all of these hysterias there are certain symptoms which are pretty uniform. We have always the uncontrolled physical movements; at least, they are supposedly uncontrolled, but presently fall into a definite movement pattern, which is characteristic of *this type of hysteria in this particular society*. Usually there is also talking or the making of incomprehensible sounds: talking gibberish. Then, somewhere along the line, there is a brief interval of unconsciousness, both at the beginning and at the end. The essential thing here is really that we have a picture of the conscious mind having abdicated. Society may explain this as being due either to the intervention of a spirit or to the absence of the individual's own soul; sometimes spirits are not brought into the explanation.

Now, in the first class, where there is no reference to spirit intervention, we have such things as arctic hysteria, so called because it occurs in the circumpolar region of the Old World. It is characterized, first, by a compulsive copying of the movements of another individual. The person who has such a seizure will copy exactly what the other individual does, no matter how ridiculous it is, and will very often repeat word for word what the other person says (9). These are the main symptoms. Now, it is interesting that there should be also another type of hysteria in this circumpolar region, in addition to the Arctic hysteria which is Asiatic and does not extend into Scandinavia, nor did it cross the Bering Strait as far as I know. The other type of hysteria in this area is associated with shamanism, and, unlike the Arctic type of hysteria, it did cross the Bering Straits. It is found among the American Eskimo, as part of the shamanistic practices which, almost without variation, did cross the Bering Straits and are also found all through the American circumpolar area.

Now, then, much further south—in Southeast Asia—we find a combination of hysterias, of a non-supernaturalistic type, in which the women suffer from what they call *latah* (64). Now, *latah* is like Arctic hysteria in its manifestations, and involves the same compulsive imitation. However, in this area this type of hysteria afflicts only women. Another interesting trait shared by both arctic hysteria and *latah* is that the same individuals are subject to repeated attacks. Furthermore, if there are two or three individuals present who have this tendency, and one of them is "touched off," the others promptly fall into the same state, which, thus, appears to be a highly contagious one.

Perhaps the most important point to be made is that, in both these areas, the hysteric is rewarded, as far as ego satisfaction goes, because he is considered funny and is laughed at. Of course, these hysterics do complain and scream, etc., and yell that the person who triggers off this state should stop his maneuvers, but—since they do become the center of attention during such seizures—they get a certain amount of ego satisfaction out of it.

I stated above that, whereas arctic hysteria is not limited to women—though it does occur with greater frequency among old women than among any other age or sex group apparently—*latah* is a woman's type of hysteria. *Amok* (*61*), on the other hand, is the man's type of hysteria and is not a repetitive phenomenon. *Amok* is, shall we say, a highly picturesque form of suicide: having reached the limit of his endurance, so to speak, the afflicted person starts out on the rampage and tries to kill as many people as possible before he is finally cut down. Now, in the old days, this orgy of murder was recognized by society, which kept an interested and admiring score of the number of people the various *amok* runners got before they were finally cut down in what must have been a highly dramatic and also highly satisfying form of exit. We can therefore think of *amok* too as a hysteria, in which unconscious aggression is frequently "put in charge" and given free expression. The best proof that we are dealing here with hysterical phenomena is that the Dutch succeeded in completely breaking up the practice of *amok*, by specifying that no matter how many individuals a man killed before they "got him," the *amok* runner was to be netted or otherwise caught, but was never to be killed. Instead, he was given a life sentence, breaking stone on the road in chains. It was this inglorious *dénouement* which finally broke up the practice of running *amok*. The same method also seems to have worked in the Philippines, where running *amok* had been introduced by the Moros and was called *juramentado*. There, too, the custom was brought to an end, but without such drastic measures.

In the Amazonian region, in the New World, there is, interestingly enough, something much like *amok*. Wagley (63) records something like *amok* for the Tapirape, though in this case the outburst does not culminate in a form of vicarious suicide. The individual simply works out his unconscious hostility by killing animals—which is not so hard to do, since these natives have a great many pets, so that there are many animals around the settlement. Thus, a man who has one of these hysteric breakdowns, which usually is the culmination of a series of frustrations, simply goes out and kills all the pet animals he can, until enough of the other men manage to jump on him and pin him down. Such a man is quite unconscious of what he is doing while all this is going on. As they say in the Chicago courts, "everything went black"—and this gives him an alibi.

The preceding cases are fairly peculiar hysteric manifestations, and there are undoubtedly plenty of others on which we have no information. At any rate these are the rather spectacular forms of hysteria which have been recorded. As stated before, this group of hysteric manifestations is not attributed to supernatural intervention, and, consequently, the only reward that the victim gets is that he becomes a focus of attention. That is enough to account for them, since, after all, that is what most hysterias are: techniques for achieving ego satisfaction.

I think, that, according to psychiatric theory, hysterical symptoms are supposed to resolve certain underlying conflicts. In addition, they are supposed to involve secondary gains, which are held to be more basic than the obvious ego satisfactions which hysteric attacks yield. I do not deny either of these views in any way. However, the ego satisfaction element is more clearly manifest in culturally patterned hysterias than are the underlying conflicts which these symptoms are supposed to resolve. This is very obvious in our society: the purpose of "hysterics" and of fainting is to get out of a conflict situation. Thus, it is really a form of unconscious self-deception, most likely to occur in an individual who has a strong superego, and finds himself in a situation which he simply cannot face. The same objective is also fairly clearly animating the Javanese. The Javanese women are the ones who do the fighting which occurs between families, etc. Now, the greatest insult which you can offer to another person in Java is to undress in front of him. So, when two angry women get excited in Java, they will first shout epithets at each other and then proceed to doff their clothes as they go on—but that is not to be considered a form of hysteria; it is merely an interesting parallel. And, by the way, there are certain strong sexual manifestations in American Indians—particularly in Indian women—for which a very interesting rationalization has been developed, and which I will take up a little bit later, because it is a semi-supernaturalistic matter.

We now come to the groups of hysterical manifestations which are interpreted as involving supernatural factors. Hysterias of this type fall into two groups. One of these is supposed to involve possession; in the other group the explanation given is "soul projection." Let me explain what this means. The individual's soul is regarded as detachable, at least temporarily, and the hysterical seizure is supposed to be an indication that the soul has actually departed. Hence, certain hysterical potentialities or inclinations of the individual readily tend to be used for shamanistic purposes. Indeed, one might say that this type of hysteria is particularly well developed in shamanism and is encouraged by society. In such seizures the shaman supposedly projects his soul at a distance and his bodily reactions are believed to be manifestations of the experiences his soul is undergoing far away from the body. This whole native theory is not unlike Flammarion's (20) mystical conception of an ectoplasmic thread which connects the astral body with the physical body.

The spirit possession hypothesis, and the projected soul hypothesis which so closely resembles Flammarion's views, are, in a sense, explanations of the same type of phenomena, one being given in what I might call extrovert and the other in what one may label introvert terms. Indeed, both are ways of explaining the withdrawal of control from the conscious mind, which gives up its place to another personality which is usually a quite partial one, and/or to unconsciousness. The two forms of hysteria—possession and soul projection—and the two explanations that go with them, may coexist in the same culture, but, as a matter of fact, for some reason such a coexistence occurs very seldom. When it does occur, the two phenomena and explanations are sharply differentiated from one another. In addition, the two types of seizures are related to different types of socially defined activities. Also, social sanction will be strongly weighted in favor of one or the other. That is, even when both occur in the same society, one will usually be considered as something of a nuisance, or the sort of a thing that old women do which is of no particular importance, while the other type of seizure will be played up by society.

In this case, too, we can plot at least the broad outlines

of geographical distribution. Possession phenomena are
found over most of the Old World. They are exceedingly
strong in Africa, in Early Europe, in the Near East and
in China. As regards India, it is difficult to say. What we
would regard as hysterical phenomena have been so completely involved in philosophic explanations and with
various schools of Indian asceticism, that it is very difficult
to get any material on this topic for India. The pattern
of this distribution suggests that the idea of possession
may very well have been an element of the old Southwestern Asiatic neolithic pattern of culture, and to have
been diffused with it. At any rate the possession complex
has been rather weak in Southeastern Asia and extremely
weak—in fact, almost non-existent—in the Asiatic circumpolar regions. You will recall here that Arctic hysteria is
not explained as possession. In America, we have a
curious situation. Real possession is extremely rare among
American Indians (59). We have a few cases of it, but
the distribution is so sporadic that it suggests that this
belief is not a result of diffusion, but an idea which has
arisen independently in various areas. What replaces
possession in America is, first of all, impersonation through
masks, costumes, etc. The individual *impersonates* the
deity, but does not actually become *possessed* by the deity.
This is simply a situation in which there is a temporary
identification of the two. It is a different approach to the
same problem. We also have, particularly among the
Northern Indians of the circumpolar group, a very interesting belief regarding the interrelation of soul and body.
The soul is defined as detachable—it has dream experiences, and so forth. This goes so far that you might say
that the Algonquin idea is really an *intermittent possession*

by one's own soul. Indeed, most of the time a person's soul is going off about its own business, and what it does mainly is to make demands on the individual through dreams. For instance, if you feel an overwhelming desire for something, it is because your soul demands it, and it is necessary for you to satisfy this need of your soul. This is an almost schizophrenic approach—a split in the personality. The same conception of the soul also appears in regard to the erotic impulse in most of the Northern tribes. For example, a woman would occasionally dream that she wanted unlimited intercourse. Since this was regarded as a demand of her soul, it did not interfere with her general status as a respectable woman, etc. She could therefore pick out a whole collection of men, anywhere from ten to twenty, and could proceed to have intercourse with one after the other, until her soul (and, we assume, her body) was satisfied. In the same way, if you dreamed of having received anything, your soul demanded it, and for an individual to refuse to give this to you was a genuine injury, since he was hurting you thereby in a vital way. There is the famous story of this kind from the early days. I think it was a Huron chief who came to the commander of a French garrison, and said that he had dreamed that the commanding officer had given him his dress uniform. Of course, under these circumstances, there was not very much that the commandant could do, except present the chief with his dress uniform. However, a few days later the commandant called on the Indian chief and said that he had dreamed that the tribe had ceded to him a particular site which he was very anxious to get to build a fort and which the chief so far had refused to give to him. The Red Brother apparently knew that his

bluff was called and that it was now up to him to cede the
site. However, after doing so, he said, "Now my brother
and I will not do any more dreaming." This cannot, of
course, be regarded as hysteria by any means, but it certainly is one of those rationalizations which can be exceedingly handy.

Now, then, soul projection is most characteristic of
the new and old world circumpolar areas, although one
gets a sporadic distribution. The soul projection theory
is much more limited in its distribution than is the missing soul belief, which is very often given as a cause of
illness. In soul loss your soul just wanders off. You
can't send your soul out deliberately, the way it is supposed
to happen in the shamanistic type of hysteria. The shaman
can send his soul out for purposes of clairvoyance, to find
out what is going on at a distance. This, by the way, is
how the Eskimo relieve the tedium of the long winter
evening. The shaman will, from time to time, send his
soul to the moon, and then have it come back to report
what people up there are doing. In other cases he sends
his soul for news to New York or to a Hudson Bay post,
and so forth. Soul projection can be used for the purpose
of magical attack. Obviously, if you can send your soul
somewhere, you can also send it out to get even with an
enemy. This technique is used in particular for the cap-
ture or recapture of souls. That is, if an individual's soul
is missing, the obvious way to bring it back is to send your
own soul after it. Your soul will track the other soul, it
will cross rivers, fight with demons, and have all sorts of
adventures which are acted out by the shaman in his unconscious state. Sometimes he works with the assistance
of bystanders; he may call on them to make a canoe for

him, whereupon they will line up and pretend to paddle, and sing canoe songs, etc. In this way the shaman's soul will cross the river and will manage to get the missing soul, bring it back, and induce it to go back into its body. This kind of soul projection is usually a very aggressive business and is supposed to be very wearing on the shaman. Hence, you find in a number of places that the shamans have developed the labor saving device of making little figures, whose souls they can send out instead of sending their own. Even in such cases the shaman will go into a trance condition and in this condition direct the search of these little souls. Both of these types of hysterias always involve stereotyped behavior, which is symbolic of the trance state, and is so defined by society. This possession-type of hysteria is utilized by the individual for the solution of various problems, or for ego satisfaction. This is a point on which I am quite sure of my ground.

Returning now to the state of possession, it is also widely used by society to provide a temporary body for supernatural beings. This makes it possible for the members of the community to address such beings directly, to get into touch with them personally, get information from them and make sacrifices to them. In other words, by this phenomenon of spirit possession, the supernatural being can become *pro tem* a present member of the society, so that people can deal with him: they can ask him questions, they can ask him for favors, they can get him to use clairvoyance to tell them what is happening at a distance, and so on. Since there is a demand for this, the individual who shows a capacity for such seizures will be encouraged and rewarded by the society. In other words, people who are able to become possessed are regarded as a definite social asset—and, of course, they are therefore also very definite assets to their families.   As one reads accounts of the "making of shamans," one finds that there take place certain uniform, or almost uniform, experiences.   For example, the shaman as a child usually shows marked introvert tendencies.   When these inclinations become manifest, they are encouraged by society. The budding shaman often wanders off and spends a long time by himself.   He is rather antisocial in his attitudes and is very frequently seized by mysterious illnesses of one sort or another.   This is almost a regular syndrome, which appears again and again in various records, and which finally leads up to the point at which the man is possessed.   In other words, all these preliminaries are regarded as expressions of the individual's resistance to submitting to the spirit possession.   But, once he gets this capacity to become possessed, he can get fees for it and, in addition, can become a person of great importance.

There are various types of possession.   The most significant one socially is the one which is directly incorporated into religious cults.   In the religions which emanate from the southwestern Asiatic diffusion center, there is a strong tendency to conflict between ritual priests and inspirational priests.   The ritual priest is the one who carries out the proper mechanics of the sacrifice, etc., while the inspirational priest is the one who, from time to time, lends his body to the god.   In Polynesia, which is a fair example of this priestly division although its culture doesn't stem from the same center, there is a term for these inspirational priests which means literally "a god-box."   In other words, such priests are containers for the deity.   As "containers" they have many advantages over a stone or wooden figure of the deity which is used in the same way, in that the god is likewise called down into it. However, when a god is in a man, the god can talk, and respond; he can make demands, tell what he wants, and so on. I may add that, again and again in the history of religions, one will find a conflict going on between these two types of priests, perhaps because the hysteric is unpredictable to the point where, as a god impersonator, he is likely to say things which are disturbing to the *status quo,* whereas a ritual priest never disturbs the *status quo.* As a matter of fact, I have some interesting examples of this in an article which I recently wrote for the Federation of Churches of Christ (45). As the conflicts were prolonged, the ritual priests usually won out, perhaps because they could continue being ritualistic longer than the hysterics could keep up being possessed. Of course, occasionally we do find an individual with the capacity for "long range" spiritual possession. Such a person often becomes a prophet and is also very likely to become a martyr in the end.

In West Africa, possession is a regular part of most cults and is aided greatly by drumming, singing, dancing, and so forth, which finally build up the subject to a state of possession. This state is characterized by definite movements.

I have heard it said that there is a striking resemblance between the movement patterns of these West African cults and those of certain Protestant cults of the southeastern United States. If this isn't a case of culture diffusion, it is certainly an amazing example of parallelism, although it would be inadvisable to mention this in the Ku Klux Klan zone. Similar examples of this form of possession may be found also in our own revivalistic cults, except that, in the latter, one is possessed by the Spirit,

instead of being possessed by a spirit god. However, the
phenomena themselves are very much the same. A friend
of mine, whose family belonged to the Holy Jumpers
cult, explained to me that they regarded themselves much
more, let us say, "restrained" than the Holy Rollers, because the Holy Jumpers, when possessed with the Spirit,
only manifested such physical phenomena as quivering,
dancing and so on, whereas the Holy Rollers also "spoke
with tongues."

Of course, there are also various types of individual
possession which are not utilized in this way, i.e., which
play no major social role. However, these need not concern us here. Instead, I will try to give you a detailed example of how "possession" works in particular types of
hysteria, and will then discuss its purpose in a particular
society which I know at first hand; and it so happens that
Madagascar (*40*) provides us with data of this type which
are as good as any.

In Madagascar there are at least two types of possession,
one of which is associated with magic and is, therefore,
so to speak, utilized by society. The other type seems to
exist predominantly for the satisfaction of individuals. In
this society the younger sons are well taken care of and
well provided for as long as they are obedient to the father
or to the eldest brother who heads the family line. They
are provided with a wife, are assured food, shelter and so
forth, but have to pay for it through subservience. In
Madagascar those younger sons who cannot put up with
this type of subservience find a way out by becoming
medicine men. The trained medicine men, called *ombiasy,* are those who, in order to get this training, were able
to wheedle the necessary money out of the head of the

family. Since this is not easy to do, diplomacy of this type calls for a very practical and very special type of personality, and, consequently, there is nothing hysterical about such men once they become sorcerers. In fact, you soon discover, when you have dealings with them, that they are an extremely hard-headed and shrewd group, who are no more subject to possession than are doctors among ourselves. The comparison is appropriate, since one might say that both our doctors and the Madagascar sorcerers are trained in the same way.

On the other hand, the younger son who cannot get from the head of the family the money he needs to learn to be a sorcerer will begin to show hysterical manifestations. The first thing likely to happen is that such a man will wake up some morning and find that a divination chart has been laid out alongside his bed. This is believed to mean that the soul of a dead medicine man wants him to serve as his "vehicle." If the chosen man doesn't want to do it—and he frequently claims that he doesn't—he just sweeps this out of the hut. However, if the spirit insists, this man will again find the chart lying on the floor. At that moment he no longer has a choice in the matter and has to become a mediumistic *ombiasy*. The *ombiasy* are especially prone to have auditory hallucinations, which usually take the pattern of voices. Some of these men that I have talked with said that, at first, their "controls" only visit them in dreams, but that, as time goes on, they will come at any time. Thus, while they are working in the fields, they may be carrying on conversations with the spirits. The *ombiasy* are exactly on a par with the trained sorcerers, since it is the success of the individual medicine man in his practice which counts here.

Now then, side by side with this professional success and serving apparently entirely the purpose of providing ego satisfaction, is the phenomenon called *tromba,* a form of violent possession which is explained as being possession by an ancestral spirit. I took the trouble to plot the distribution of *tromba* as far as I could find out about it, and among the Tanala, with whom I lived, I found no cases in which either a family head or a medicine man of either variety was afflicted with *tromba.* The incidence of *tromba* was highest among childless widows. One might have almost anticipated this finding, since childless widows are the lowest group socially, and therefore the most subject to frustration. I also noted that younger sons, who did not become either medicine men or warriors, were also subject to *tromba.*

According to information I got from people who had experienced *tromba,* this seizure usually followed a period of frustration and of conflict. Eventually the increasingly disturbed individual would be conscious of a mounting tension. Suddenly everything would waver in front of his eyes. Then the individual becomes unconscious for a brief period, falls down and then picks himself up again and begins to dance. Sometimes he goes directly into a dance without this momentary unconsciousness. In this region the manifestation of *tromba* is dancing, and the possessed person must have someone to dance with him.

I must stress that the spirit which possesses the dancer does not announce himself. He is a disembodied human spirit, though not necessarily a spirit of the subject's own ancestor, although the dancer is able to do more with it if it does happen to be an ancestral spirit. Sometimes, however, it is only the spirit of the *zumba,* one of the "aborigines."

The most important thing is that, as long as the person is possessed, all his orders have to be fulfilled under pain of incurring the hostility of the spirit. An old woman will, during the *tromba,* demand that people come and dance with her, and this means that drummers must be summoned immediately . . . and, of course, drummers must be paid, and so must the dancers. I know that an old woman, who seems to be rheumatic and decrepit, will dance sometimes for forty-eight hours at a stretch, and dance down one partner after another, so shifts of dancers and of drummers have to be provided. The possessing spirit may also demand to have an ox sacrificed to it. This is an awful blow for these people, who hate to kill their cattle; it is like asking that a barn be burned down, since cattle are their main investment. While all this is going on, the possessed person is absolutely "sitting on top of the world." In the end, the medicine man is called in. After the possessed person has pretty well worked himself out, the medicine man puts various medicines in a large cowhorn filled with good cold water and, when he thinks that the auspicious moment has come, he tells the spirit it is time to go. Then he takes this hornful of water and dashes it in the fact of the possessed, who passes out cold. Presently the subject "comes out of it," picks himself up and the *tromba* is over—until the next time.   Individuals who have this form of possession are regarded as a nuisance, because one can't really get anything out of the spirits. Therefore, their demands are a sort of supernatural blackmail. Yet, one can readily see that such seizures work to the advantage of the possessed, since the family is rather reluctant to cause them to have a *tromba* seizure by frustrating them. It is also extremely interesting to note that when one person in a village gets *tromba,* if there are any other people in the village who are subject to it, they too immediately develop the same symptoms. This in itself suffices to make *tromba* a perfectly recognizable form of hysteria, since, everywhere where we have beliefs in possession, crises of possession are exceedingly contagious.

Phenomena of this kind are not limited to primitives. Our own ancestors had collective manias, or group hysterias, which were of a very startling sort. In medieval Europe we had the dancing manias, for instance. I am not sure whether we can say with complete certainty that the flagellants were also hysterics of this class, but they assuredly were at least something pretty close to it, as were unquestionably the various witch manias.

Coming back once more to the Malagasy, I have to mention a third type of hysterics which are to be found among these people, who seem to be well equipped along this line. These are the *komasave* or malignant witches, who are apparently somnambulistic. Our information concerning these witches casts a great deal of light on the sort of thing that went on in Europe during the time of the witch persecutions, because in Madagascar, and also in most of Africa, it is believed that the witch commits his wicked deeds *unconsciously.* At any rate, these *komasave* are night runners. They come and stand outside the house where a person lies sick, and wail and cry for the dead, thereby causing the ailing person to die. They also dance on tombs, break down crops, ride cattle to death, and the like—and do all this without knowing that they do it. Let me stress that this is not just native folklore. I know of some actual cases of this kind in which individuals did go through all of these (culturally prescribed) forms of malicious behavior, without knowing at all that they did it. They would do all these deeds at night, and would only be conscious that something odd had been going on because in the morning, when they wakened, they found that they were tired and scratched with thorns.

Turning now to a broader historical panel, most of us know that the early European pattern of ecstatic states existed side by side with demonic possession. In medieval Europe there was a belief in possession by the Spirit, which led occasionally to the phenomenon of the stigmata. In other words, certain mystics would go into ecstatic states and would actually develop stigmata like those of Christ. This, by the way, was not just a medieval superstition! It is as well attested a phenomenon as anything can be at that period. In addition, we know perfectly well that this can also be done by hysterics. Now then, somewhere on the borderline between regular possession by spirits and the mystic experience is perhaps the place where we have to put the mediumistic hysterias, which still flourish even among ourselves, and differ from the other forms in that bodily passivity is usually assumed. The idea behind this is that there is a need for complete passivity, and complete withdrawal, in order to encourage the "controls," who either speak through the body of the subject or else draw upon his body energy or ectoplasm, which they can shape in various ways. Such mediumistic phenomena are widespread, but are usually demonstrated only by minor practitioners. Although they rarely are the center of an organized religion, they do flourish at least on the outskirts of our culture, and it is an interesting fact that *the stories which are told about psychic phenomena are curiously uniform all over the world.* Thus, "stunts" of ecoplasmic materialization have been recorded for culture after culture. The well known "spirit rattles" are likewise very common phenomena, and so are the voices which come from different directions. Whether you are dealing here with some inherited patterns of charlatanry or whether you are dealing with some phenomena which have some basis in fact is, I think, still an unsettled question. Now then, coming back for a moment to the "soul projection" shamanistic patterns, here the initial symptom is always loss of consciousness with spasmodic movement which is then followed by the acting out of the journey or progress of the soul in disembodied form. Here, too, we have plenty of "talk with spirits," i.e., communication with spirits whom the shaman meets in the course of his soul-travels and which enables him to bring back the desired information.

So much for the general cultural background. In conclusion, the only thing that, I think, needs to be emphasized is that hysterical phenomena are everywhere very decidedly culturally patterned. In fact, if one knows a culture, one can predict what form hysterias are going to take in that society—or pretty nearly so. This is the strongest possible argument in favor of the thesis that, whatever the etiology and dynamics of hysteria may be, its symptoms are extensively and intensively shaped by culture.

Bibliography

1. AUBIN, H.: Introduction à l'Etude de la Psychiatrie chez les Noirs. *Annales Médico-Psychologiques*, 97:1–61, 1939.
2. BATESON, GREGORY and MEAD, MARGARET: Balinese Character; A Photographic Analysis. *New York Academy of Sciences Special Publication*, 2, 1942.
3. BENEDICT, RUTH: *Patterns of Culture*. Boston, Houghton, Mifflin, 1934.
4. BOAS, FRANZ: *The Mind of Primitive Man* (Rev. ed.). New York, Macmillan, 1938.
5. CANNON, W. B.: "Voodoo" Death. *American Anthropologist*, n.s., 44:169–181, 1942.
6. CAROTHERS, J. C.: The African Mind in Health and Disease. *World Health Organization Monographs* 17, Geneva, World Health Organization, 1953.
7. CHAPPLE, E. D.: Measuring Human Relations. *Genetic Psychology Monographs*, 22:13–147, 1940.
8. COOPER, J. M.: The Cree Witiko Psychosis. *Primitive Man*, 6:20–24, 1933.
9. CZAPLICKA, M. A.: *Aboriginal Siberia*. Oxford, Clarendon Press, 1914.
10. DENNIS, WAYNE: *The Hopi Child*. New York, Appleton-Century, 1940.
11. DEVEREUX, GEORGE: Institutionalized Homosexuality of the Mohave Indians. *Human Biology*, 9:498–527, 1937.
12. —: A Sociological Theory of Schizophrenia. *Psychoanalytic Review*, 26:315–342, 1939.
13. —: (Review of) KARDINER, ABRAM: The Individual and His Society. *Character and Personality*, 8:253–256, 1940.
14. —: Logical Foundations of Culture and Personality Studies. *Transactions of the New York Academy of Sciences* Series 2, 7:110–130, 1945.
15. —: *Reality and Dream: The Psychotherapy of a Plains Indian*. New York, International Universities Press, 1951.
16. —: Cultural Factors in Psychoanalytic Therapy. *Journal of the American Psychoanalytic Association*, 1:629–655, 1953.
17. —: Primitive Genital Mutilations in a Neurotic's Dream. *Journal of the American Psychoanalytic Association*, 2:484–492, 1954.

18. DOLLARD, JOHN: *Caste and Class in a Southern Town.* New Haven, Yale University Press, 1937.

19. DuBois, C. A.: *The People of Alor.* Minneapolis, University of Minnesota Press, 1944.

20. FLAMMARION, CAMILLE: *Les Forces Naturelles Inconnues.* Paris, E. Flammarion, 1907.

21. FORTUNE, R. F.: *Sorcerers of Dobu.* New York, Dutton, 1932.

22. FREUD, SIGMUND: Obsessive Acts and Religious Practices. *Collected Papers* 2, London, Hogarth, 1924.

23. GORER, GEOFFREY: *The American People: A Study in National Character.* New York, Norton, 1948.

24. GUINARD, J. E.: Witiko among the Tête de Boule. *Primitive Man,* 3:69–71, 1930.

25. HALLOWELL, A. I.: Fear and Anxiety as Cultural and Individual Variables in a Primitive Society. *Journal of Social Psychology,* 9:25–47, 1938.

26. HENDERSON, D. K. and GILLESPIE, R. D.: *A Text-Book of Psychiatry* (new ed.). London, Oxford University Press, 1944.

27. HERSKOVITS, M. J.: *Dahomey; An Ancient West African Kingdom,* 2 vols. New York, Augustin, 1938.

28. HILL, W. W.: Notes on the Pima Berdache. *American Anthropologist,* n.s., 40:338–340, 1938.

29. HOLLINGHEAD, A. B. and REDLICH, F. C.: Social Stratification and Psychiatric Disorders. *American Sociological Review,* 18:163–169, 1953.

30. KARDINER, ABRAM and LINTON, RALPH: *The Individual and His Society.* New York, Columbia University Press, 1939.

31. KARDINER, ABRAM: *The Traumatic Neuroses of War.* New York, Hoeber, 1941.

32. —— and LINTON, RALPH: *The Psychological Frontiers of Society.* New York, Columbia University Press, 1945.

33. KLEIN, MELANIE: *The Psycho-Analysis of Children.* London, Hogarth, 1932.

34. ——: *Contributions to Psycho-Analysis, 1921–1945.* London, Hogarth, 1948.

35. KNOWLES, N.: The Torture of Captives of the Indians of Eastern North America. *American Philosophical Society Publications,* 82:151–225, 1940.

36. KOBLER, FRITZ: Description of an Acute Castration Fear Based on Superstition. *Psychoanalytic Review,* 35:285–289, 1948.

37. LANDES, RUTH: The Abnormal Among the Ojibwa. *Journal of Abnormal and Social Psychology,* 33:14–33, 1938.

38. Laubscher, B. J. F.: *Sex, Custom and Psychopathology*. London, Routledge, 1937.

39. Lewis, Oscar: Manly-Hearted Women Among the North Piegans. *American Anthropologist* n.s., *43*:173–187, 1941.

40. Linton, Ralph: The Tanala. *Field Museum of Natural History, Anthropological Series*, 22, 1933.

41. ——: *The Study of Man.* New York, Appleton-Century, 1936.

42. ——: A Neglected Aspect of Social Organization. *American Journal of Sociology*, *45*:870–886, 1940.

43. —— (ed.): *Acculturation in Seven American Indian Tribes.* New York, Appleton-Century, 1940.

44. ——: *The Cultural Background of Personality.* New York, Appleton-Century, 1945.

45. ——: *Manuscript* (Prepared for the Federation of Churches of Christ) n.d.

46. Malinowski, Bronislaw: *Sex and Repression in Savage Society.* New York, Harcourt, Brace, 1927.

47. Mead, Margaret: *From the South Seas.* New York, Morrow, 1939. (3 vols. in 1.)

48. ——: *And Keep Your Powder Dry.* New York, Morrow, 1942.

49. ——: *Male and Female.* New York, Morrow, 1949.

50. ——: The Swaddling Hypothesis: Its Reception. *American Anthropologist* n.s., *56*:395–409, 1954.

51. Michelson, Truman: The Autobiography of a Fox Indian Woman. *Bureau of American Ethnology, Annual Report*, *40*:291–349, 1919.

52. Orlansky, Harold: Infant Care and Personality. *Psychological Bulletin*, *46*:1–48, 1949.

53. Plant, J. S.: *Personality and the Cultural Pattern.* New York, Commonwealth Fund, 1937.

54. Radin, Paul: *Crashing Thunder.* New York, Appleton, 1926.

55. Sapir, Edward: *Selected Writings of Edward Sapir* (D. G. Mandelbaum, ed.). Berkeley, University of California Press, 1949.

56. Sewell, W. H.: Infant Training and the Personality of the Child. *American Journal of Sociology*, *58*:150–159, 1952.

57. Stainbrook, Edward: Some Characteristics of the Psychopathology of Schizophrenic Behavior in Bahian Society. *American Journal of Psychiatry*, *109*:330–335, 1952.

58. Stayt, H. A.: *The Bavenda.* London, Oxford University Press, 1931.

59. Stewart, K. M.: Spirit Possession in Native America. *Southwestern Journal of Anthropology*, *2*:323–339, 1946.

60. Tooth, Geoffrey: Studies in Mental Illness in the Gold Coast. *Colonial Research Publications* 6, London, His Majesty's Stationery Office, 1950.

61. Van Loon, F. H. G.: Amok and Latah. *Journal of Abnormal and Social Psychology, 21*:434–444, 1926.

62. Van Wulfften Palthe, P.: Psychiatry and Neurology in the Tropics (in) Liechtenstein, A.: *A Clinical Textbook of Tropical Medicine.* Batavia, de Langen, 1936.

63. Wagley, C. W.: *Personal Communication.*

64. Yap, P. M.: The Latah Reaction. *Journal of Mental Science, 98*:515–564, 1952.

Index

This Book

CULTURE AND MENTAL DISORDERS

By

RALPH LINTON

*was set and printed by The Mack Printing Company
of Easton, Pennsylvania, and bound by Arnold's Book
Bindery, Reading, Pennsylvania. The page trim size
is $5^3/_8 \times 8$ inches. The type page is 23×37 picas.
The type face is Linotype Caledonia, set 11 point on
13 point. The text paper is 70 lb. Westvaco Eggshell.
The cover is Bancroft's Oxford 1999.*

With THOMAS BOOKS *careful attention is given
to all details of manufacturing and design.* It is the
Publisher's *desire to present books that are satisfactory
as to their physical qualities and artistic possibilities
and appropriate for their particular use.* THOMAS
BOOKS *will be true to those laws of quality that
assure a good name and good will.*